POPULATION DYNAMICS
International Action and Training Programs

POPULATION DYNAMICS

International Action and Training Programs

Proceedings of the International Conference on Population, May, 1964, The Johns Hopkins School of Hygiene and Public Health

Edited by

MINORU MURAMATSU and

PAUL A. HARPER

THE JOHNS HOPKINS PRESS   Baltimore, Maryland

Preface

∙∙∙

This book represents the proceedings of the International Conference on Population at the Johns Hopkins School of Hygiene and Public Health in May, 1964. The purpose of the Conference was to bring together persons responsible for action programs in family planning with those responsible for training public health personnel, to exchange information and discuss mutual problems.

Related papers were presented in groups of three or four, and each group was then discussed for an hour. The participants were requested in advance to question freely and critically; therefore the discussions add considerable value to these proceedings.

The Keynote Address by the President of the Population Council gives a perceptive appraisal of recent developments and current problems in this rapidly expanding field. This is followed by papers on action programs in India, Pakistan, Japan, and Korea, countries which then had official policy to promote family planning.

The pilot program to introduce the new intrauterine devices (IUD's) in Taiwan is discussed, as is the decline in birth rate among the Chinese populations of East Asia. Other papers describe the current status of action programs in the United States and Puerto Rico. A study of provoked abortions in Santiago, Chile, provides startling evidence of the magnitude and seriousness of this method of family limitation and the factors which drive people to it. The value of studies of attitudes toward contraception and the knowledge and use of contraception in promoting voluntary and official family planning programs is discussed.

Action programs require a multidisciplinary staff that includes administrators, clinicians, demographers, social scientists, and physiologists. Most of these persons obtain their basic professional training in schools of their own discipline and then come together in schools of public health for postdoctoral training to work as a team in family planning. Current developments in such training are the subject of the final group of papers by a social scientist, a physiologist, and a public health educator.

The volume concludes with an address given by the Assistant Secretary of State and Assistant Administrator for Human Resources and Social Development, Agency for International Development, which describes United States government policy as of May, 1964.

This whole field is developing with extraordinary rapidity. There have been many conferences and books on the demographic situation and the implications thereof. This publication complements these, providing both worker and student with a succinct description of action programs around the world at a time when they were relatively new.

P.A.H.

Contents

Opening Address

ERNEST L. STEBBINS

I want to take this opportunity to greet you and to express our very real appreciation to all of you who have made the effort to come and join us in this discussion of action programs and population control and the training of personnel for these activities. This Conference is due largely to the interest of a number of people.

On behalf of The School of Hygiene, The Johns Hopkins University, I would like to express our appreciation to the many people who have made this Conference possible.

Dr. Homer Calver was one of the first who was interested in a conference such as this one, and through him Mr. Hugh Moore has not only shown great interest in the subject but has contributed necessary funds. We are very grateful to both Dr. Calver and Mr. Moore. We are also deeply indebted to the Population Council, as they have given us a great deal of guidance over the years in the development of our population control training program and have also given us much advice and assistance in the development of this particular program.

I cannot miss this opportunity to express appreciation to one of my favorite students, Dr. Marshall C. Balfour, who came to Hopkins as a young man in 1947 and selected population as his area of study. He has been at it ever since and never failed to make the point that public health workers and schools of public health were very remiss in not giving greater emphasis to the subject. I also want to thank him for the help that he has given us in his broad experience in various parts of the world in the selection of speakers on this subject.

Our sessions will deal with action programs in population control. I think that most of us feel that there has been tremendous progress made throughout the world in the tackling of this problem. We are not going to talk about how serious the population problem is. That has long ago been amply demonstrated. Our purpose in this Conference is to consider the action programs in those countries where there are national policies concerning population control. We have selected for our speakers people who are knowledgeable in the field and who have been directly associated with an action program, and we want to emphasize the action side in our discussion. Finally, there will be consideration of the training aids for the people that will be involved in population studies and action programs in various parts of the world.

We are particularly fortunate in having as our keynote speaker Dr. Frank Notestein, who needs no introduction to anyone who has ever considered population as a problem. Dr. Notestein, as you know, has been in the field almost for his entire professional life. He worked with the Milbank Memorial Fund and then developed the program of population studies at Princeton University. In 1959 he became President of the Population Council and has intensified his work in the field since then.

Keynote Address

FRANK W. NOTESTEIN

It always gives me great pleasure to come back to Hopkins, an institution early in the vanguard with studies of population. My first experience goes back to Raymond Pearl and Lowell Reed, and I am tremendously encouraged to see that the early patterns they set are now being re-established.

I am particularly pleased that you have limited the scope of this Conference and will talk basically about (*a*) the nature of action programs, and (*b*) the problems of training for the support of such programs.

I want to address myself to the nature of the problem, which raises questions of strategy and tactics, and then to the implications of the answers to these questions for training—training of whom, for what purpose, and where.

First, as to the nature of the problem, uncontrolled fertility raises the population growth to a rate of from 3 to 4 per cent as soon as there is little more than minimal health protection.

Uncontrolled fertility means that more than 40 per cent of the population will be under fifteen years of age. This combination of rapid growth and youth presents major obstacles to fundamental economic modernization, to the immediate improvement of living conditions, and even to political stability. Man's best hope that economic modernization will permit sustained improvements in health and education and political freedom lies in his ability to reduce birth rates with something like the speed that he can now reduce death rates. Some such proposition surely represents the premise on which this Conference is based.

The most interesting thing in this context is the expanding demand for assistance in the reduction of fertility throughout the world. Ten years ago few of us would have dreamed that world opinion would move so fast. Ten years ago, one spoke very carefully, very cautiously and tentatively about the need for reducing birth rates, especially in foreign countries. That time is past. Today it is not people of the West who are pushing the world: the rest of the world is pushing us, and the challenge is one to which we are only beginning to rise. There is a great expansion of interest in birth control. The United Nations' position on issues of technical aid is instructive: when it came to a vote in 1962 virtually all of Asia and the entire Arab world wanted technical assistance in birth control. The core opposition was in European countries: Ireland, Belgium, France, Italy, Portugal, and Spain, all of which have extremely low birth rates. This position seems to me to be a very fortunate one politically. It was not a case of people with low birth rates trying to force their behavior on the rest of the world. It was the governments of people with high birth rates who pounded the table saying, "You must help us do what you have already done." In a sensitive world this situation could not be more fortunate.

The demand for assistance and the need for technically trained personnel is tremendous. It is no longer possible to fulfill our obligations by wringing our hands and saying that the population problem is going to be terrible. The job of doing something about it is on us.

Turning rather briefly to the problems of strategy, these always include assembling political support and involving critical groups. Strategy involves education of the public in ways that support changes in individual behavior, and it involves the solution of specific problems in the distribution of services and supplies. There must be a balance in the allocation of resources between gaining the involvement of political leadership, the education of the public, and the solution of problems of method, supply, and administration. The balance always depends on the situation with respect to govenment policy, which substantially determines the part that foreigners can play.

It is hard to overemphasize the importance of gaining firm political support by widening the areas of intellectual involvement in the countries concerned. The problems will be difficult at best. There needs to be more than just a decision on the part of government. Broad-based support from the articulate public is required. And how does one obtain it? My impression is again that exhortation and quasi-ideological speeches are rather uninfluential, least of all the exhortation and ideological speeches of foreigners.

Our task, I think, is quite evident. It is to help the facts speak for themselves. That is, in demography, to work with planning boards, using our slide rules to find out the requirements for employment, the need for migration, the problems of home building, the problems of education. Surely these facts speak much more eloquently than any exhortation concerning the abstract nature of the problem.

Secondly, our task lies in medical research, which seeks better methods for the control of fertility and makes the physiology of reproduction an exciting and intellectually respectable subject in medicine, arousing the physician with an intellectual challenge that might very well give stimulus to the routine practice of obstetrics-gynecology.

In sociology, with surveys of knowledge and attitudes or practices concerning reproduction, we can find out what people really know, believe, and do, not what their leaders simply suppose is the case. All of us here with field experience recognize the fact that on these topics today the public is often ahead of its leaders, and this is true for the United States and its government as well as for the people in foreign countries. We have just had an exciting example that may be more heard of in Turkey, where Dr. Berelson was presenting the results of a survey concerning reproductive knowledge and behavior. The Turkish government's enthusiasm was almost unlimited because it did indeed turn out that the substantial majority of women, even in the conservative parts of the country, was in favor of birth control, as were the religious leaders of the area, in about the same degree.

One could multiply this kind of example all over the world. It gives the political leader evidence that he is not really running a risk in taking a new position, that he is operating in consonance with the wishes of a substantial sector and often a majority of his constituency.

It seems to me that birth control movements have shown a naïve preoccupation with methods. We experiment with one method, and when it does not work after half a trial, people get discouraged and say, "My, my, we need a different method." With the next method the same thing happens, and the same thing happens on down the line. Always we conclude that the method is wrong, when in fact the difficulty has been equally a weakness of motivation.

One cannot read the demographic record of Europe without realizing that the folk methods of birth control brought the birth rates down initially and are still of substantial importance. One could almost say that the decline of the birth rate caused the invention of modern contraception; this makes as much sense as saying that the invention of modern contraception caused the decline of the birth rate. The desire to limit fertility certainly stimulated the development of the various inventions.

That all populations have known effective means throughout history of controlling their fertility and that some have used them and some have not must suggest that there are problems of wider scope than those involving the gadgetry. The method is of course important as well, but I want to re-emphasize the proposition that the problem of altering people's behavior and giving adequate normative support to the altered form of behavior also lies at the core of our concern. All too little is known about this.

What is the best mixture of the informational versus the hortatory content in the educational effort? Clearly it depends on the time and the place. My impression is that efforts to emphasize information, at least initially, and to play down the preaching aspects repay themselves. I feel that in the initial stages of a program information that permits the people already motivated to fulfill their objectives provides the best seeds and opens the best channels for communication and for further alteration of behavior patterns.

Similarly, the problems of service and supply of contraceptives will depend on government policy, but service and supply to the already motivated is, as I suggested, the best means of communication. Incidentally, we have given far too little attention to commercial channels for the distribution of supplies, as opposed to governmental programs.

We have forgotten that in the experience of the Western world government policies have had a negligible effect, that birth control has occurred because ordinary citizens, against the advice of all respectable and responsible leadership of church, state, and medical profession, have decided that it is wise. They have taken it up and have found ways of solving the problem of supply, largely through commercial channels.

I do not want to suggest that I am against governmental programs. I am only saying that in thinking about these problems we have given too little attention to administrative problems. We in the Population Council used to say that the problem of changing the attitudes of the peasants was the most important problem. Quite frankly, I am inclined to think that influencing the peasant is going to be easy compared to the task of changing administrative services of the government. It is not enough to indoctrinate our students with nice modern charts demonstrating the best possible administrative procedures and then assume that we have solved administrative problems.

We have to start with the administration in every country at whatever stage of advancement it has achieved, and it is usually appallingly backward. Our people have to know not only how things are done in theory, but how they really get done under any administration and how one copes with this kind of problem. These same considerations are central to training problems.

Finally, in all of these areas—in the involvement of the community and in research, in public education, and in the matter of supplies—there is the question of the role of foreign assistance. The donor agency may be international or governmental or academic or a private foundation. The best type of support depends on the climate of opinion in the receiving country. In general, advocacy cannot be the role of the foreigner, especially where personal values are involved. One may doubt the wisdom of substantial help in providing contraceptive supplies. Technical help in this field is certainly important and experimental and pilot projects are useful, but the job of solving the total supply problem is inevitably a job that the government itself or the people themselves must take on. Aid on a massive scale in terms of supply can easily be misinterpreted, and there are cases where I suspect it would do more harm than good to have an outside agency, particularly an outside government, giving aid in the form of contraceptive supplies.

Moreover, this aspect of the problem is not terribly important because it represents a minor part of the total resources that need to be brought to bear. On the whole it seems to me the government aid in most cases could stop well short of the actual mass supply of contraceptives. Foundation and academic aid in general might well stop with the technical aspects—the demonstration, training and assistance in administration—and could leave the explicit burden of the public relations problem to the national groups themselves. Here, the local members of the international private action groups, notably the International Planned Parenthood Federation, can be particularly valuable. This is a group that can enable the people of the country involved to do such hortatory work as seems useful.

Sensitivities in these areas are changing very rapidly. Things can and ought to be done now which could not be and ought not to have been done five years ago. Change will continue to be very rapid, and it would indeed be worthwhile if we could establish principles for our respective organizations to follow in the changing stream of events. I am afraid, however, that these principles will be very hard to identify.

Turning now to tactics, there are a couple of points I would like to make. Efficiency in family planning programs is essential. Very simply, it is not sufficient to find out that a program works. The resources are limited and the needs are unlimited. We must endeavor to learn how to stimulate as much birth control practice as is possible for the money. This will require effective communications, administration, and supply.

We will need to demonstrate as soon as possible the effectiveness of the pilot projects and of the initial efforts to bring in the necessary political support. The importance of this cannot be overemphasized. It is entirely possible that birth control could have the beginning of success while the national birth rate continues to rise. If health through the villages is improved a little, reducing spontaneous abortion and lifting the birth rate enough to cancel out the initial impact of birth control, the fact that the pilot projects, the initial efforts, are successful can be concealed. Yet the early identification process is necessary. In many countries the solution to the problem will be slow. The people should be able to see that they are getting something for the effort. This suggests the importance of baseline surveys and of sensitive indicators concerning the effect of pilot projects.

It would also be useful if someone after this Conference could summarize the state of our knowledge. In this field of tactics, there is a very great danger that knowledge will not be accumulated. We are making some effort in the Population Council to inform people about the various experiments that are going on in various countries, but it will no longer do to wait six years for the massive book to come out: the field is moving too rapidly and the information will be obsolete before publication occurs. It is important that we have better accumulation of our recorded experience, and I doubt that this accumulation has thus far been accomplished.

With regard to training, most of the personnel involved in family planning programs have to be trained in their own countries, but I want to discuss training in the U.S., for both the U.S. and foreign services. The demand is mounting. Any of us who are trying to staff foreign operations are aware that the problem of getting suitable personnel is important. Not only must one find a person willing to serve abroad, but he must also be technically competent and know how to express himself colloquially and discreetly in a foreign language. It is difficult to find this combination, and the number of people needed will increase rapidly.

It is clear that a wide range of skills is needed in demographic, economic, sociological, social psychological, and statistical work, and in the fields of public health administration, maternal and child health, and health education. Furthermore, there is the obstetrics and gynecology group and the whole biomedical range. They will work with ministries of public health because these are the groups usually assigned to the task. Partly because of the somewhat intensive snobbery in that field it is important that these people be medical. In view of the exaggerated attention the world gives to working papers and union labels and licenses, they must receive certification, and the schools of public health must provide this function. But what training shall they get? This is a highly controversial subject, and I am sure that in this medical-dominated environment a social scientist must tread carefully.

To work with a situation that is changing rapidly, how narrowly specialized should such people be? Surely, for most of the workers their training can be narrowly specialized, but this kind of training is best done in the country concerned. The schools of public health will only be dealing with a highly select group that will have a much more general task. They will be dealing with the men who want to make public health their profession and family planning their specialty, but then what kind of training is right for this group? I cannot stop thinking that our schools of public health are still overconcerned with the biological and medical aspects of the problem; they tend to operate as if the major problem was that of changing the environment, while in part it is that of altering individual behavior.

I get discouraged when I find Asians sent to this country to acquire the standard materials in public health and supposedly some specialization in family planning who have never been exposed to any substantial portion of the literature on population or human fertility and the experiments in the introduction of birth control. They often seem to be knowledgeable about epidemics and viruses and bacteria and to know all the technical words, but to be innocent to the point of superstition about human fertility. This is an impossible situation. Personally I think that a health officer can get intellectual discipline in his training program and still have training that is relevant to the subject matter involved. Even further, it seems to me that the field of birth control, which requires such emphasis on changing individual behavior, should provide especially relevant training for public health officers who, as environmental matters get to be handled with increasing ease, must find larger and larger proportions of their time devoted to the area of personal behavior. In short, the modification of educational programs needed for the proper training of health officers to become administrators of birth control programs are, I suspect, the modifications needed to meet the emerging needs of the entire public health field.

The need to train officers in family planning will and must force the schools in the direction that they need to go. I hasten to say that Hopkins seems to be at least aimed in these directions, but I put it negatively on purpose, because Hopkins has gone far enough. Progress has been substantial, and I trust that one result of this Conference may be an emphasis on the ways in which the needed changes of curriculums can come about.

Finally, I wish to emphasize again that the world climate has changed rapidly in ways that make effective work possible. This change in the attitudes of governments has come with a speed that ten years ago we did not think possible. Public awareness is progressively greater throughout the world.

Research in the steroid pills and the intra-uterine devices has given us new and powerful methods which are suitable for the needs of many situations. This alters the picture considerably. When I mentioned the importance of motivation, I did not mean to suggest that weakly motivated people do not need effective methods. We are in the process of a real breakthrough, and as a result it seems to me we can predict that action programs vigorously pursued can in many instances bring drastic reductions in the birth rate.

Population growth need no longer be the rock upon which all efforts to plan for economic and social development are wrecked. Solutions are presently in sight if we give the leadership, which has to date been lacking. The schools of public health have a great and unfulfilled role to play.

PART I

ACTION PROGRAMS

1

India's Family Planning Program: Some Lessons Learned

MOYE W. FREYMANN

The purpose of this paper will be first to provide a brief general description of the family planning program in India and then to try to draw from the Indian experience some generalizations regarding problems of developing family planning programs. Comments will be offered, also, on some of the implications of the Indian program for possible supporting activities by schools of public health in the United States.

Nature of the Indian Family Planning Program

Since the beginning of the century a steady decrease in death rates has occurred in India while birth rates have remained high, resulting in an estimated current rate of growth of 2.3 to 2.4 per cent per year. Although it is difficult to quantify the effects of various casual factors behind the decrease in mortality, a principal and obvious factor has been the increased availability of food. Distribution of food supplies has been greatly facilitated during this century by improvements in transportation and in civil administration. Furthermore, production of food has been augmented and made more regular by development of irrigation works and relaxation of internecine conflicts and oppressive taxation. Since India's independence, during the decade 1951–61, the per capita net availability of food grains in India rose from an estimated 13.5 ounces to 16.2 ounces per day. More recently, specific

13

efforts to control disease, notably the malaria eradication program, are also becoming important, along with food availability, in widening the gap between mortality and fertility.

The beginnings of an organized family planning program can be dated in the nineteen-thirties, when India was influenced by the movement for women's emancipation, the worldwide economic depression, and the ferment associated with the independence movement. Social reformers and political leaders began to promote the specific idea of family planning, and higher-class families began to limit their size.

It was not until India achieved independence in 1947, however, that the full implications of its population explosion were felt by economic planners in the government. A cautious program of research and clinical services was included in the First Five Year Plan development period and served to reassure a sensitive young government that such activities were politically feasible. During the Second Plan period (1957–61) a Central Family Planning Board was formed and a Director of Family Planning was posted in the Health Ministry. Family planning boards and state family planning officers were also located in each of the states.

At the beginning of the Second Plan period, the principal model available for use in expanding the field program was the traditional family planning clinic, which sought to attract female "clients" to come to a center for a relatively complete medical and contraceptive service. Liberal grants-in-aid were therefore made available to private and official agencies interested in developing such facilities. By the end of the Second Plan, over 4,000 clinics had been set up. However, even though contraceptives were issued at subsidized rates or without cost, this clinic approach was found to reach only a very small fraction of the people. During the Second Plan period efforts were also made to raise the national awareness of family planning through distribution of information and development of films and exhibits. Civic-minded leaders in each state were appointed as "honorary family planning educators" to help mobilize local interest and support. Subsidies were also made available for village leaders' camps to encourage local participation.

Since the Indian states are relatively autonomous in their health activities, there was irregular progress in development of state programs. The central government employed special training teams for assignment to each state to help provide orientation in family planning for existing health and rural development workers. Training centers for more senior personnel were developed in Bombay and Delhi, and the states established their own small centers for junior clinic personnel.

In states where there was strong administrative and political support for the program the use of voluntary sterilization was promoted and was well received. In Maharashtra state, temporary "camp" hospitals have been used, while Madras has concentrated more on the use of regular clinical facilities for this purpose.

Also during this period a major effort was made to strengthen the foundations of the national program through development of national advisory committees for demographic research, for research on medical and biological aspects of reproduction, for communications, and for research. Centers were developed for work in each of these fields.

During the early part of the Third Plan period, in 1962–63, the Director of Family Planning made a major effort to pull together the observations of family planning workers throughout the country plus various research findings, with the goal of reformulating the entire family planning program on the basis of the experience thus far accumulated. The summary of this analysis and a proposal for a reorganized program was presented in the report of the Director of Family Planning for 1962–63. This was approved by the Central Family Planning Board, and in October, 1963, the revised pattern was adopted as the basis for the official program of subsidies for family planning activities throughout the country. Since the formula of central subsidies to the Indian states now covers from 75 to 100 per cent of program costs, there is pressure on the states to adjust to the new pattern, and this process is now under way.

In a further effort to clarify the problems of implementing this reorganized program, and to plot further action, the Central Family Planning Board also set up in late 1963, a special Family Planning Program Evaluation Committee; its report is expected in the fall of 1964. This Committee has formed study groups for various substantive areas of the total program, such as medical and biological research, social legislation, and public education. In addition, it has provided for special evaluation teams to visit the states. Each team spends a week in a state studying the organizational aspects of the program there in use. These teams have considerable value in stimulating interest in the program and in helping to interpret it. They are also systematically uncovering and reporting upon specific problems of implementation.

The new "extended family planning program" pattern, which is now being developed, has adopted the over-all goal of reducing the national birth rate from 40 per 1,000 to 25 per 1,000, as soon as possible. Three operational objectives have been adopted which are deemed necessary for the achievement of the over-all goal. These operational objectives, having as their target 90 per cent of the married adult population of India, are as follows:

1. *Group acceptance.* Individuals should know that their immediate social group feels that a smaller family size is the normal, desirable behavior for members of that group. The underlying assumption is that, without this, most couples will hesitate to adopt contraception; with it, most couples will somehow change their behavior in the direction of the norm.

2. *Knowledge about contraception.* People should acquire information about the feasibility of efficient contraception, about specific methods, and about the salience of family size to the achievement of their various personal values. It is assumed that such information will hasten the adoption of family planning by innovators in the population as well as the diffusion of the small family norm and of effective contraceptive practices.

3. *Availability of supplies.* Any person should feel that he can obtain simple contraceptive supplies with minimal physical, financial, or psychological barriers. It is assumed that this will strongly reinforce the other two objectives and will itself foster more efficient contraception.

For the achievement of such objectives, it is proposed that the present organizational structure of the program be greatly strengthened. The District (containing 1 to 2 million population) is now the critical developmental and political unit in India. At this level, the District Health Officer's staff will be augmented by a medical family planning officer, a health educator, and statistical and supply personnel. Within the District, the primary operating unit for developmental activities is the Community Development Block (containing 70,000 to 100,000 population). Here will be posted a male family planning extension educator, a person having a college degree plus special training in extension education methods in family planning. Under him would be at least two junior, male field workers. The nurse or health visitor posted in the primary health center would be the basic female worker for family planning at the Block level. The number of auxiliary nurse-midwives posted in the villages would be augmented, when possible, up to a ratio of at least 1 per 10,000 population, in order to permit them to expand their maternal and child health activities to include family planning. Also, as a matter of policy, indigenous mid-wives will be encouraged to participate in the program.

The male extension educator would be expected to spend a substantial portion of his time working with other types of community development and health workers, in order to mobilize and to facilitate their contribution to educational and supply activities. Special attention is also to be given to working with Block-level leaders to stimulate their responsibility for planning and implementing the program in the Block. In the villages, the peripheral workers again would primarily be engaged in helping to identify potential local leaders, providing them with information and supplies, and assisting them in developing family planning promotional activities and contraceptive distribution within their own groups.

A statistical clerk will also be posted at the Block level to help strengthen the recording and transmission of vital statistical data and to participate in periodic evaluation activities. In addition, a full-time storekeeper would be responsible for maintaining a flow of supplies.

For urban areas, a similar strengthening of staff and reorientation to nonclinical approaches is proposed. Also, in association with the development of this reorganized program, research activities are focusing more on development of improved methods of evaluating program impact. Under the Indian Council of Medical Research studies of newer methods of contraception, including intra-uterine devices, are under way.

To sum up, the family planning program in India has evolved to a point where it has adopted an organizational pattern, based on extensive field experience, which primarily emphasizes community-level educational approaches and availability of supplies. Clinics are now considered to be best used only as referral sources for occasional problem cases. Finances sufficient to support such a reorganized program are available, as are the basic recruits who can be trained to meet the additional staff requirements. The program could make excellent use of the present contraceptive technology and, in addition, would provide the essential structure for applying any further advances in such technology.

However, in addition to the adoption of a sound organizational pattern, three other major elements or problem areas must be amply provided for before the total program can move strongly ahead. One such problem is the contraceptive supply line. As yet, rubber contraceptives are not manufactured in India, and they have not been introduced in the very wide network of commercial distribution channels which now extend into rural areas. The Indian government is presently taking steps to assure local production of inexpensive, good quality materials. A special committee, including marketing specialists from Indian industries, is now evolving a plan whereby wide distribution of a subsidized, standard-quality product could be introduced through commercial supply channels.

A second major area requiring attention at this time is the central family planning organization, which must be strengthened to provide the necessary leadership, stimulation, and guidance to the augmented state activities. Steps are also being taken toward this end. In addition to the strengthening of executive staff, an important addition to the technical leadership has been the development of a Central Family Planning Institute. Also, a new National Institute of Health Administration and Education has been established; this will be especially concerned with building the administrative and educational skills needed in order to provide a strong organizational framework for the extended family planning action program.

The third additional element now required is an aggressive, imaginative training program aimed at reorienting existing personnel and training the large numbers of new workers who will be needed, at various levels, in the augmented family planning program. In addition to the efforts of the National Institute of Health Administration and Education and other higher-level faculties, it is now further proposed to develop as many as fifty family planning field training centers throughout India. Each such center would relate to the training needs of the family planning program for approximately 10 million people. Although India has shown its ability to handle tasks of such magnitude, there will undoubtedly be serious problems in moving ahead quickly with so huge a training program.

Some Lessons Learned

The generalizations presented below are broad and oversimplified; all of them are not universally applicable even in India. However, each can be supported with evidence drawn from different parts of India. Their presentation in this form can at least serve the purpose of sensitizing family planning workers to look for their possible applicability in other situations. There will be need to elaborate, test, and further refine such concepts and principles as the art and science of the family planning program development progresses.

1. *Political and policy support.* A critical first step in program development is the provision of demographic data which bears directly on the problems of national economic development, so that economic planners are sufficiently alerted to problems of population growth. Survey data indicating the degree of general receptivity to the program among the population have also served in India to reassure politicians and government officials. Simple pilot projects which demonstrate that there is good popular acceptance of family planning information have also served this purpose.

Involvement of voluntary agencies in the action program at the outset may help a great deal in creating a climate of official approval. This has presented some distinct dangers, however. The tendency for voluntary associations to depend on clinical methods of approach and to concentrate primarily on women may divert the program from more productive channels. Also, vested interests among private agencies may ultimately become barriers to building tightly knit and technically sound activities as a part of the over-all government development program. In general, the most productive activities for private agencies have been in the field of mass education; they can, also, contribute very usefully to experimentation in newer and somewhat sensitive areas, such as family-life education in schools.

2. *Pilot projects.* Social research activities on family planning in India have gradually tended to shift away from surveys of knowledge, attitudes, and practices relevant to fertility control, toward involvement in pilot projects which aim primarily at formulating an effective program to introduce family planning, through the application of the best available educational and organizational talent to the problem. In the latter situation, the social researcher focuses more on assessment of the total impact of the program on the target population and on the clarification of problems of program implementation through limited "diagnostic" studies. It is noteworthy that, in this context, the use of the term "communication research" has had to extend beyond the meaning of public opinion research to include studies of a variety of factors that can influence the educational impacts of an action program. Educational problems in a country such as India are strongly bound up with the whole process of developing a new *system* which can catalyze the

social and psychological changes needed for fertility reduction. There-fore, communication studies must deal with the analysis of vertical and horizontal lines of communication within the official organization, as well as with analysis of the problems of communication of field workers with the public and of lines of communication within the village society.

3. *Social legislation.* The potential for facilitating certain types of social legislation which could influence fertility rates is still relatively unexplored. In India, several types of recent social legislation may tend to support higher fertility. A number of scholars have urged that special attention now be given, for example, to legislation which might increase the number of women in the labor force, raise the age at marriage, reward small families, or increase the proportion of school-going children. But exhortation to pursue such possibilities does not help much. On the other hand, further social research might be extremely helpful. For example, those who are now interested in liberalizing the abortion laws in India are frustrated because of the almost complete lack of data on the incidence of induced abortion or on the attitudes of people toward abortion. What is needed is solid, locally collected information which clarifies the basis for and the implications of such proposed legislation.

4. *Program evaluation procedures.* Present methods for detecting changes in fertility patterns are very crude, as are methods for measuring possible intermediate variables such as changes in family size norms, information about contraception, or the extent of use of contraceptives. If improved methods can be made available, their use in detection of differentials between subgroups in a given population may produce useful hints for framing action programs. More sensitive measurement of the effects of action programs would be of tremendous help in learning operational lessons from these experiences.

Even with the present methods, however, a great deal can be gained by insisting on specific statements of goals and objectives at the early stage of program planning and by providing for continuing evaluations of various aspects of the program. The technique used in malaria programs of having external observers analyze the field operations annually can be usefully applied to family planning programs.

5. *Supply needs.* A major problem in the Indian program is to make better use of contraceptive methods which are already known. For example, there is a steep rise in the use of condoms in rural and urban family planning programs in India, but there are still serious problems

with the breakdown of supply lines. An important lesson is that provision for an adequate and assured supply line at the very *outset* of a program is of primary importance. The presence of available supplies itself has an educational impact. A small proportion of the population in most areas is usually ready to utilize contraceptive materials if they are available on a continuing basis; if this group cannot be supplied, then the effect of educational activities may indeed be negative.

In the Indian program, heretofore, contraceptive materials have been purchased by official or private agencies from the open market for free or subsidized distribution. This has been expensive, has resulted in irregular quality, and has produced some confusion when people receive different types of materials at different times. To overcome these problems, it has seemed to be much more advantageous to prescribe a certain standard of quality and a standard packaging for government purchases. The Indian program is coming to the point of strongly urging development of local production, either private or government sponsored, in order to help maintain low prices and to encourage local initiative in distribution through commercial channels.

6. *Contraceptive technology.* Field trials with oral contraceptives in India have thus far shown poor acceptance of this method. Trials with intra-uterine contraception, on the other hand, show promise of high acceptability. However, among medical people there are still some reservations about this method, on the grounds that it is accompanied by a high prevalence of cervical erosions and by bleeding among women who are already anemic. A major principle which emerges from Indian experience is that leaders in the medical profession must themselves experiment with and endorse improved contraceptive methods in order to convince their colleagues and government officials to practice contraception. Outside pressures or assertions that a method is useful in the population of another country are not a substitute for independent experience by local professionals.

Voluntary sterilization of males and females has been shown in India to be capable of achieving popularity as a family planning method. In some large population groups, the rate of sterilizations has reached the level of 2 to 5 per 1,000 population per year. It has proved to be safe, effective, and easy to bring to the people. The "camp" method of bringing such services to the people in rural areas might in the future be used also for intra-uterine contraceptive methods. Thus far the people seeking sterilization have usually been those who already have a relatively large number of children, and the direct demographic impact of this method alone is not clearly known. However, as Sheps and others have recently emphasized, there is considerable intrinsic value in a highly efficient contraceptive method. In addition, it is important to note the secondary, educational effect of the intra-uterine method. In the organization of the sterilization "camps" especi-ally, a great deal of community action and communication occurs, which increases the salience of the family planning movement for all members of the community. The ones who volunteer for sterilization are, in essence, dramatizing to their neighbors their own feelings about the importance of limiting family size. For every sterilization per-formed, it may be hypothesized that some other couples are moved in the direction of adopting contraception of some type.

Obviously, new contraceptive methods which may be more effective and easy to use will be most welcome and can help a great deal to accelerate progress of the program; all possible efforts should be made to develop and make such methods available. However, even then, a basic organizational structure will be needed for program implementa-tion; the structure now being set up in India can be easily adapted to any contraceptive improvements now foreseeable. It should be remem-bered, also, that individuals will inevitably vary in their preference for different methods; being able to adjust to these different preferences, through making available a variety of methods, will have a positive value in accelerating the program.

In India, as well as elsewhere, some persons tend to seek "one answer" solutions to population problems, hoping for a pill, or device, or an educational gimmick which will solve everything. This innocent approach can be destructive when it leads to delays or hesitation about moving ahead aggressively with the application of the knowledge and experience already available. The fact is that population control can be achieved efficiently with present methods, even nonmechanical meth-ods. Even in rural Indian populations, after a certain point, there is ample evidence of common usage of birth control methods; this point, however, may not be reached until a relatively large number of births has occurred.

7. *Roles of doctors.* Many observers of programs in the Indian states, as well as in other countries, have criticized the part played by doctors in the total process of program development. Surely the young medical graduate, who is almost entirely clinically oriented in most countries, is inadequately equipped to diagnose and minister to community-level needs for family planning program development; he reflexively re-

gresses to the classical clinical concepts. Medical reluctance to build up responsibility among other types of workers and among the public for informational and supply distribution aspects has also been a serious barrier at times. A further problem is a tendency for over-recording and insistence on more follow-up than is needed in a mass program.

The extended family planning program in India is now dealing with this problem by defining the role of the clinic as a referral service for the occasional case needing special medical consultation. Hopefully, training in medical colleges and orientation of medical people concerned with the program will also support the mass approach. This problem will probably remain, however, as a price to be paid for the advantages of being legitimized by association with health programs and of being able to channel family planning education and distribution services through the whole network of rural health workers.

8. *Educational activities.* Educational efforts may be categorized according to two main functions: that of influencing family size norms and that of providing specific information about contraception. For each of these functions the educational content, channels, and methods may vary considerably according to the situation in a particular population group.

For influencing family size norms, certainly the examples and statements of public figures are of great significance. The involvement of public figures may also help to keep the program from becoming a political issue. The norm-setting process can also be assisted through use of mass-communication methods which help to legitimize the small-family style, to provoke conversation, and to establish a vocabulary for discussion of family planning. In addition, Indian experience has indicated the need for special efforts to catalyze the process of change within various subgroups in a total population which may be accustomed to following norms which are unique to themselves. For this purpose, a most useful technique has been to help the members of local population groups themselves to identify persons of their group whom they might look to for further information about family planning. Such internally selected leaders can then be given special orientation courses; they may also act as agents for contraceptive distribution. Such group members can, with help, be much more effective than any outsider in the direct promotion of family planning within the group.

Provision of specific information about contraceptive methods, their effectiveness, safety, and advantages can be provided through written materials, local exhibitions, and the use of trained leaders, as noted above. Local health workers such as midwives or sanitarians may also be useful as sources of such information. Again, helping group members themselves to realize that other members in their group are interested in this subject and helping them to discuss it will foster person-to-person diffusion of specific knowledge about contraception.

9. *Organizational problems.* In the Indian program, as in others, carefully laid plans have faltered, even in closely supervised pilot projects, because of the problems of establishing the strong organizational framework which is needed to place trained people in the field and provide them with adequate supervision and administrative support. A need which is obviously fundamental to the total program, but which merits continuing emphasis, is the preparation of workers who are specifically equipped for the functions they are required to perform as part of the total program and the development of supervisors for them who are skilled in the process of setting local program priorities, in identifying and relating to personnel in the health department and other agencies of the area, and in mustering and co-ordinating the resources which are needed for an effective operation.

Training Needs

Efforts to assist in meeting training needs for such programs must be built upon a careful analysis of local situations in the country to be assisted and must carefully avoid inappropriate preconceptions. A number of assertions or principles, which might be considered as guideposts for educational assistance to India's family planning program, are discussed below.

1. *Family planning administrators and educators.* The immediate need of the Indian program has been for skilled health administrators and educators who can rapidly apply what is already known. Optimally, basic training for such persons would be given in their home country or as near to it as possible. They need forceful preparation in the principles, concepts, and methods of health administration and health education. Unfortunately, postgraduate public health institutions abroad, as well as in the U.S., are not as strong in these fields as is desirable. The urgency of further equipping family planning action personnel adequately in these fields poses a challenge to U.S. schools of

public health to build up their own programs of teaching and research in administration and education and to try to relate them to overseas situations. It should be emphasized that, especially in underdeveloped countries, the problem of developing family planning programs goes far beyond the classical bounds of maternal and child health programs; the students should not be led to conceive of such programs only in the framework of maternal and child health services.

2. *Training of trainers.* Directors of state family planning training centers or those bearing major training responsibilities in other situations have need not only for basic concepts of education and administration and for family planning technical content, but for pedagogical skills in curriculum planning, development, and evaluation. This will require a considerably more specialized program than for the general administrator or educator.

3. *Researchers.* Fundamental research training is more easily transferable from country to country; it is wise to plan for longer periods of training for students in fields basic to family planning. Their special projects should optimally be related closely to program needs. For example, the statistician or demographer who spends the major part of his time with a school of public health may prepare himself especially for identifying biological factors related to changes in fertility trends. He should also learn something of the vocabulary of the health field and of the administrative and educational aspects of the program to which he must relate.

4. *"Higher level" leaders.* The more senior family planning officials are a separate problem: they should be freed for a visit abroad, for several months at the most, in order to gain from the stimulation of exchange of ideas and to explore new avenues of action and research. Schools of public health can assist by arranging discussions with faculty and students, scheduling observations of official agencies in their area, and demonstrating how research and training activities of public health institutions relate to ongoing programs in the field.

Summary

This paper has presented a brief sketch of the development of India's national family planning program. Recently, as a result of careful study of experiences thus far, India has developed a revised program pattern which especially emphasizes community-level educational approaches and easy availability of contraceptive materials. Adoption of this clearly defined and rational master plan is itself a major advance. Attention is now being turned to strengthening three essential elements for the implementation of this plan: an adequate contraceptive supply line, a firm organizational base, and a massive training program.

From experience in a variety of localities in India a number of broad generalizations may be made about the process of family planning program development in a country of this type. Such generalizations are offered with regard to problems of establishing political support for a family planning movement, the roles of pilot projects and social research, and the subject of supporting social legislation. Propositions are also offered regarding program evaluation procedures, contraceptive supply lines, contraceptive technology, and the role of doctors. The needs for differentiating educational functions and for providing an optimal organizational environment are also noted. No claim is made for the universality of these assertions. However, in the early stage of growth of a discipline (in this case the discipline of family planning program development) such propositions are needed in order to sensitize the practitioner and to stimulate the researcher.

The paper further extrapolates from needs in the field and suggests some guidelines for U.S. schools of public health, which may wish to contribute through educational services to family planning programs abroad.

2

Population Problems in Pakistan: Program and Policies

NAFIS SADIK

Pakistan came into existence as a result of the partition of India in August, 1947. It consists of two separate areas, East Pakistan and West Pakistan, separated by a thousand miles of India. The total area is approximately 365,000 square miles, of which West Pakistan is approximately 310,000 square miles and East Pakistan is 55,000 square miles. The two areas of the country differ in climate, topography, language, and cultural characteristics, but they are alike in religion, in their dependence on agriculture, and in their standards of living. For example, in West Pakistan, the rainfall varies from 7 inches in Karachi to about 19 inches per year in Lahore; the two major crops are wheat and cotton and the staple food is wheat. In East Pakistan the average rainfall varies from 75 inches to 115 inches per year, the two major crops are rice and jute, and the staple food is rice. The language in East Pakistan is Bengali, which is understood by most of the population, while in West Pakistan there are several languages, but Urdu or some derivative of Urdu is generally understood throughout the country.

The demographic picture in Pakistan is clouded by the incomplete recording of births and deaths and by the inaccuracies of census taking, especially in remote rural regions. It is estimated that as many as 50 per cent of the births and deaths are not reported. At the turn of the century, the area which now comprises Pakistan had a population of about 46 million. The population at the time of partition, when there was much rioting and mass killing, was estimated at 70 million people.

27

The projections of the First Five Year Plan (1956–60) were based upon successive estimates of the rate of population growth; in 1955, this was calculated at 1.5 per cent per annum (later raised to 1.7 per cent). It was quite apparent after the 1961 census that the growth rate was higher than had been previously estimated and an annual rate of increase of 2.2 to 2.6 per cent was widely accepted. The most recent projection prepared by the Planning Commission gives an annual growth rate of 2.7 per cent.

Because of these problems it was decided to develop improved machinery for the continuous collection of data on vital statistics.

TABLE 1: ESTIMATES AND PROJECTIONS OF GROSS NATIONAL PRODUCT
AND SELECTED POPULATION CHARACTERISTICS,
PAKISTAN, 1949–85

	1949–50	1959–60	1964–65 (Estimate)	1974–75 (Projection)	1984–85 (Projection)
Gross national product (in Rs million)	25,000	31,600	40,000	70,000	130,000
Population (in millions)	79	99	113	148	186
Growth rate (per cent per annum)		2.6	2.7	2.8	2.0
Per capita income [a] (in Rs)	316	319	354	473	700
Per cent, population under 14		46	48	48	44
Primary school children (ages 6–11, in millions)		15	16	21.5	26.5

[a] Gross national product/population.

Population growth estimate areas were established and comprised ten sample regions in each wing. Registration of births and deaths in these sample populations is done by local registrars. Their reports are checked against a census which is taken every three months by interviewers (from outside the village). These two groups of workers, the registrars and the census interviewers, each work independently. The data from these twenty population growth estimate (PGE) areas suggests that the annual rate of growth may be 3 per cent or more. Preliminary estimates from the PGE areas place the birth rate between 50 and 60 and the death rate from 20 to 30. More precise estimates put the birth rate at 57 in East Pakistan and 52 in West Pakistan. The death rate is placed at 31 in East and 26 in West Pakistan. There is more general acceptance of the estimates of the birth rates than of the death rates. Many demographers believe that the death rates have declined rapidly and are lower than those given above. It is not improbable that the growth rate may be anywhere between 3 and 4 per cent. In any case, the demographic outlook is quite bleak, and at the current rate of growth we shall double our population in less than thirty years. The great importance of this in making projections of future needs for such things as food, housing, schools, and medical care is self-evident. The ultimate aim of economic development is to raise the level of living of the individual. The achievement of this goal is made more difficult in countries such as Pakistan, which, in addition to being poor, have a rapidly increasing population, since any increase in the national income is swallowed up by the population increase. For example, in the Second Five Year Plan (1961–65) the national income is expected to increase by about 26 per cent but the per capita income will only increase by about 11 per cent, to an annual per capital income of Rs365. This is indeed a meager increase when judged by the efforts, sacrifices, and investments put into it. As the Queen said to Alice: "It takes all the running you can do to keep in the same place."

As in many other countries, the first step in promotion of family planning was taken by volunteer family planning groups. The first such group was formed in Lahore in 1952 and in East Pakistan in 1953. The government gave financial and verbal support to these organizations. It was, however, soon recognized that the government must assume the chief responsibility if the effort was to meet with success. To this end, a sum of Rs500,000 was allocated by the central government for promotion of family planning. This nominal amount was for the purpose of providing practical help to those people who wanted to practice family planning on their own. Later, in 1959, the first pilot project on family planning was approved by the Economic Committee of the Cabinet at the cost of Rs900,000. In 1960, after consultation with the Population Council of New York, a comprehensive scheme for family planning was included in the Second Five Year Plan, which ran from 1961 to 1965, at a cost of Rs30.5 million.

This plan has four major aspects: (1) Training in family planning methods and techniques for a yearly minimum of 1,200 technical health personnel, including doctors, nurses, midwives, and health visitors. This training was to be carried out by the five provincial training-cum-research institutes. Attached to these institutes are mobile training teams whose job it is to educate other personnel at village quarters. (2) An intensive education and publicity campaign for family planning by the central and provincial governments. (3) To provide family planning services to 1.2 million people by July, 1965, through the existing health services as a normal function of these services. (4) Research and demonstration projects in the field of family planning. Figures 1 and 2 show the administrative set-up of the family planning program.

These were ambitious goals for a developing country with great

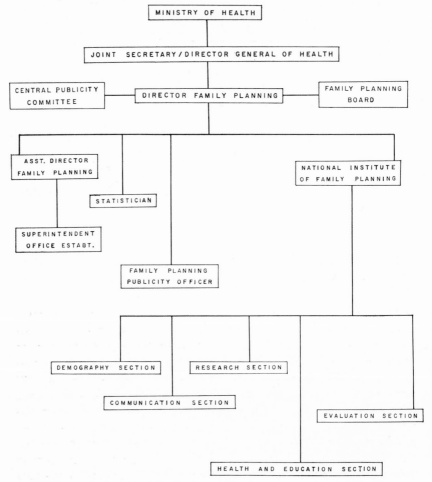

Figure 1. Central set-up for family planning, Ministry of Health, Pakistan.

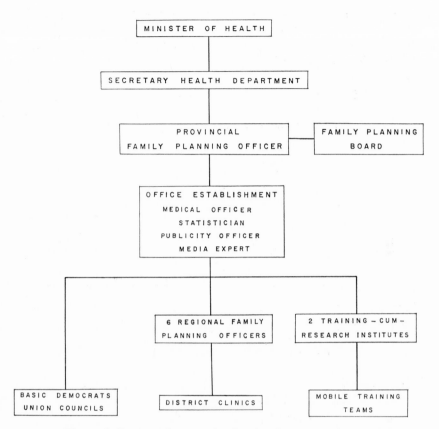

Figure 2. Provincial set-up for family planning, Pakistan.

burdens and great shortages of trained administrators and professional workers. Indeed, it is not an exaggeration to say that some of the goals were unrealistically high. It is now estimated that only 60 per cent of the budget will be used by the end of the Second Five Year Plan period in 1965 and that the level of attainment of the goals will be about 40 per cent. These are preliminary figures, and it is too early to make a firm evaluation; nevertheless, it is quite apparent that the program has not yet succeeded in lowering the birth rate. Under the program 2,750 family planning clinics have been started; these have given contraceptive advice to approximately 1 million people. Almost 2,000 medical personnel have been trained in family planning technique. A National Research Institute at the central level and five training-cum-research institutes at the provincial levels are functioning. Attempts to publicize and popularize the program have, however, been ineffective as can be seen from the record of clinic attendance, which has always been very poor and is now declining. The contraceptives promoted on a national scale were the traditional methods—foam tablets, condoms, diaphragms, jellies. Though all hospitals are equipped to carry out sterilization (i.e., vasectomy and tubal ligation), these facilities have not been used by the population.

Some of the barriers to a family planning program are given below as an introduction to a discussion on research. Here it may merely be said that there were few or no precedents to guide us and that the program had to be developed from scratch. Other countries with comparable problems and difficulties that have attempted to promote family planning have not found any easy road to success. Our own shortcoming should be looked upon as the first faltering steps of an infant program that must first learn to walk before it can run.

The experience of the family planning program of the Second Five Year Plan should be viewed as a pilot period for the Third and Fourth Five Year Plans. We now have better understanding of the problems and difficulties. We have a nucleus of trained personnel, and there is much more general awareness of the importance and urgency of the problem. The recent week-long international meetings in Lahore to discuss Pakistan's population problem were a great success and received nationwide coverage in newspapers, magazines, and on the radio. This awareness of the problems is spreading from the leaders of the central government through all levels of administration and society to the local leaders and citizens in the towns and villages. We have developed an administrative framework on which we can build.

We have sixteen different research projects on family planning in various parts of the country. One of the most important of these is the National Study of the Intrauterine Contraceptive Device (IUD), which is being conducted by the National Research Institute of Family Planning. One of our great needs is for an effective contraceptive that does not require repeated action by the user, that is inexpensive, relatively free of side effect, and that can be discontinued when a couple wishes to have another child. Preliminary reports suggested that the IUD met most of these requirements, and therefore the National Research Institute of Family Planning was able to launch its study. The objectives are to obtain information about the acceptability, effectiveness, safety, and cost of the IUD. There are thirteen groups participating in the study, most of which are in departments of gynecology and obstetrics in the teaching hospitals. A preliminary report as of December 31, 1963, is as follows: The use effectiveness of IUD seems to be quite high especially in the people who are in the literate groups. Incidentally, the intra-uterine devices used are the Lippes' loops and Margulies' coils. Recently there has been discussion over the need to switch to Birnberg's bows, which cannot be removed by the user. We do not really have enough cases in our study but the general concensus is that perhaps we have found a solution; it will be a solution only if the preliminary examinations, etc., are not a prerequisite to use and if insertions can be done by paramedical personnel.

I shall now try to review some of the reasons why family planning meets with so many problems in Pakistan. Children in Pakistan are considered an economic asset. They are referred to as "blessings of God." This is not without some justification; in an average family a child is sent to work at an early age, sometimes even at nine or ten years of age, and is an additional source of income until he gets married and has his own family. Secondly, children are also old-age assets: they provide and look after their parents when they are old and unable to earn. Thirdly, infant mortality is still so high that people are not really sure that their children will grow up. Until these concepts change, and until we can find some way to demonstrate to the average person that an excessive number of children is an economic burden, I feel that adequate motivation for widespread family planning may not be possible.

There are a number of questions that must be raised regarding the program as presently set up. For example, is it administered too much as simply a normal function of existing health services in the country? It may be pointed out that the health services in urban areas are limited and practically nonexistent in rural areas where the majority of the population lives. The doctors and technical personnel in these services are already overworked and find little time to devote to family planning. Furthermore, the average health person is trained to consider treating illness as more important than anything else. The motivation aspect of the program has not been promoted. It is encouraging that plans now being formulated call for more specialists who, while working within the pattern of existing health facilities, will be giving their full professional attention to the family planning program. Also it seems right that the number of physicians and other professional persons additionally trained for work in this area is increasing. Careful consideration must be given to drawing increasingly on governmental or private resources outside health directorate channels.

Population control is rightly assigned the priority of a national emergency. This calls for the mobilization of all available resources. A tentative allocation of Rs150 million has been made for the family planning program in the Third Five Year Plan, 1966–70. The role of the government will fall into three categories:

1. The provision of service facilities.

2. The provision of information, inducement, and education.

3. The provision of supplies.

This is an all-embracing role. Family planning will be integrated into the entire development policy, planned programs, and service systems in the country. All public and private agencies and institutions will be utilized; for example, the health services, the social welfare and community development projects, the social education projects, the basic democracies, education departments, industrial and commercial areas, agricultural extension services, semigovernmental agencies, voluntary agencies, and the ministries of Finance, Information, and Broadcasting.

The program must always be subject to review, using a decline in the birth rate as a criterion of effectiveness. It is hoped that from the various research projects now under way new and effective modifications of the program will be suggested and continuous referral to the effect on the birth rate will be possible. It has been worked out by our economists that for the family planning program to have any impact on the economic situation, the birth rate must be halved in twenty years. This is a formidable task, but within the realm of reality.

In a free country, decisions such as the size of one's family are personal ones; therefore, only when there is widespread awareness of the benefits that accrue to the individual through a limited family can our goals be realized. It is, therefore, necessary to educate all those in positions of authority, leaders who are in contact with the people, all professional people, so that they give wholehearted support both in words as well as actions to the program. Education of people who influence public opinion and are perhaps in a way fashion setters therefore assumes great importance. Rational thinking on the size of a family should become a part of our way of life.

3

MESOREP Program in Lulliani, West Pakistan

ROWLAND V. RIDER

The name MESOREP is an abbreviation of Medical Social Research Project, which is a demonstration-research unit of the National Research Institute of Family Planning of Pakistan and is the project with which we at this School are associated. In broad terms its purpose is to provide infomation of use to the government of Pakistan in carrying out the national family planning program.

The project is supported by a grant-in-aid from the Ministry of Health of the central government of Pakistan and by private foundation funds administered by the Population Council. It is governed by an autonomous executive committee consisting of representatives of the central government of Pakistan, the provincial government of West Pakistan, the University of the Panjab, The Johns Hopkins University, and the Population Council. This committee reviews and approves project plans, job descriptions, salary ranges, and budgets.

The scientific aspects of the project's work, the design and conduct of studies approved by the executive committee, and the day-to-day direction of the project are the responsibility of the project director and the joint director.

There are many problems in staffing, administration, and training that arise in the operation of a field research unit such as this, and some of these problems may be inferred already even from this simple introductory description of its organization. Of course, part of the specific function of the project is to determine, examine, and, in so far as possible, solve similar problems as they are found in the operation of an active family planning program.

The function of this paper is simply to present MESOREP's history to date in order to provide additional illustrative background for an

35

understanding of training needs for planning, developing, and operating a family planning program in a country such as Pakistan.

MESOREP, located in West Pakistan, is one of two such units, the other being the Health Education Project of Dacca, East Pakistan, with which the University of California School of Public Health is associated. The Population Council was instrumental in initiating each and in bringing about their association with U.S. schools of public health.

The project director of MESOREP is Dr. John C. Cobb of the faculty of the Maternal and Child Health Department of The Johns Hopkins School of Hygiene and Public Health. Dr. Cobb arrived in Lahore to take up residence in January, 1961. In May, 1961, a Pakistani public health physician, Dr. Rasheed Ghazi, became joint director; and in August, 1961, Dr. Harry Raulet, an anthropologist, also a member of the M.C.H. Department of Hopkins, arrived in Lahore and has since served as director of the social studies section of the project. Also in 1961, Dr. John Kantner, a demographer on the Population Council staff, joined the group in Lahore and stayed for two years as special consultant to MESOREP and as visiting professor at the University of the Panjab.

Since these men arrived the staff has steadily grown and has been at approximately its present size for something over a year. At present, the full-time staff numbers twenty-three:

13 professional Pakistani research workers:
   3 physicians
   1 registered midwife
   1 sociologist with some demographic training
   8 with special training in social work, soci-
      ology, or education
2 faculty members from Johns Hopkins
8 Pakistani administrative and clerical personnel

There are also several part-time employees at all levels, the number varying from time to time.

Before describing the activities of MESOREP it is necessary to begin with a brief description of the geographical setting of MESOREP. MESOREP early decided to concentrate its efforts in a rural setting, and the town of Lulliani was selected. Lulliani is a town of some 12,000, located about 25 miles south-southeast of Lahore. Lulliani has some of the characteristics of an urban area, but it is on the whole more representative of rural Pakistan. It is located on the main road from Lahore to Kasur and is near the Indian border. Lulliani is a trading center with a small hand-loom industry. It is in the center of an irrigated agricultural area. About 90 per cent of the population is Muslim; the remainder is Christian. About 30 per cent of the Muslims immigrated from India following partition.

A primary demonstration health center is located on the edge of the town and, with three subcenters in nearby villages, serves an area with about 50,000 people.

In addition to Lulliani and the three villages where the health subcenters are located, there are several other villages in which MESOREP has been active. Only one will be mentioned at this point, namely, Chamrupur, which has served as the pilot area for procedures used in Lulliani or elsewhere.

It will be convenient to discuss the program of MESOREP under three headings: Education (or Motivation); Distribution; and Observation (or Data Collection, Analysis, and Interpretation). Of course this separation for the sake of simplifying the discussion is somewhat arbitrary and unrealistic because the nature of the project's goals requires unusual overlapping and interaction among these elements.

Education (or Motivation)

The educational program, or the program to increase motivation for family planning, has elements varying from very concentrated and direct procedures to general and almost incidental activities. It will be impossible to detail all motivational activities but most of them may be included under the following four headings: the training of local volunteers, mass meetings, home visits to "highly eligible" couples, and health center activities.

Training local volunteers. The purpose of the program is to obtain a group of trained local volunteers, both men and women, to support and help create a sense of community acceptance for the family planning program, to carry out direct family planning educational work in the community, and to serve as agents for the distribution of contraceptives. This program is expected to provide information on such problems as recruitment of candidates for such work; development of curriculums and audio-visual aids; arrangement of details concerning time, place, and frequency of meetings; and the effect of such programs in similar villages and small towns of West Pakistan.

The volunteers were recruited to be representative, married resi-

dents of Lulliani, preferably literate and relatively influential; they had
to give verbal consent to attend the courses and later to assist
voluntarily in the family planning program. By the time of the selection
of candidates the staff members had become fairly familiar with the
town as the result of frequent visits for surveys and other activities,
and, with the help of town committee members, the selection was
made.

Details of the curriculums cannot be given here. There were two
courses, an initial or elementary course and an advanced course. Each
course had five weekly sessions aimed to cover the "why," "what," and
"how" of family planning. The advanced course went into more detail
and in particular devoted more time to techniques and practices of
using the various flip charts, flannel board stories, and other visual aids.
Certificates were given after satisfactory completion of the courses; of
136 men and women (including 28 *dais* or local midwives) invited to
the initial course, 51 received elementary certificates and 43 others
received the advanced certificates.

Evaluation has been of two sorts: (1) informal staff discussions of
each session; (2) formal interviewing of the volunteer group and of
clients, i.e., acceptors of contraceptives. Interest, attendance, and rate
of learning of volunteers were above expectation. Many clients have
stated that the volunteers were their source of knowledge regarding
contraception. Volunteers are known to have defended the general
program when criticized. It is clear, however, that the volunteers need
continued encouragement.

Mass meetings. Two outdoor, evening mass meetings have been held
to which the entire town was invited. At each meeting attendance was
estimated at about 2,000. The first meeting featured the presentation of
certificates to the volunteers who had completed the training courses.
On both occasions the theme of family planning was developed by use
of film strips, movies, and talks (including participation of the volunteers) interspersed with movies or comedy skits with entertainment as
the primary goal. Evaluation has been attempted by more or less
subjective staff interpretation and by postmeeting interviews of at-
tendants.

Home visits. As an experiment in direct persuasion of individuals
thought likely to be most receptive, a schedule of home interviews of
couples selected as "highly eligible" was arranged and followed. The
general criteria were that the couple must be married, living together,
wife under forty-five years of age, and with three or more living

children. A random third of the approximately 700 highly eligible couples was not visited. Of those visited, the wife in every case received at least one visit by a female social worker. Some of these couples received a subsequent visit by a male social worker to the husband, and a smaller number of the wives received a follow-up visit by a female social worker. The social workers had a broadly prescribed outline for their discussions which included asking some questions about contraception and pregnancy status and then discussing family planning, giving special emphasis to intra-uterine contraceptive devices (IUD's). Referral chits were given to those who said they were ready to come to the health center, and the lady social workers indicated on which days they would be available at the health center to receive women who came in.

Much analysis yet needs to be done, but the visits appear to have been responsible for about 40 per cent of the IUD's that have been inserted in the highly eligible couple group. Because the proportion of highly eligible couples receiving such insertions is small, however, this form of motivation is relatively costly.

Health center activities. The health center itself is the center of most of the formal educational, training, and distribution activities. Through such conventional methods as talking with patients and the use of posters, the center is potentially always carrying on the job of education. It was felt that the better the health center performed its usual functions of medical care, the better were its chances of promoting any new service, specifically family planning. Therefore, MESOREP has considerably augmented the program at the health center as follows. The joint director has for the last year worked three or four days per week as a medical officer, a gynecologist on the MESOREP staff has operated a gynecological clinic two or three days a week, and a pediatrician from one of the Lahore hospitals has been present one day a week for a pediatric clinic. These individuals are expected to take whatever opportunities present themselves to answer questions and make suggestions regarding family planning.

Distribution

The distribution of contraceptives started about one year after MESOREP began studying and becoming acquainted in Lulliani. Distribution has been primarily at the health center, though some distribution of conventional contraceptives has occurred through commercial channels, through the trained volunteers, and through health center personnel when visiting the health subcenters. Records are available for health center distribution and for residents of Lulliani; the acceptors can be identified in detail by place of residence and many other demographic or social characteristics, including membership in the highly eligible couple group. Through January, 1964, about 10 per cent of the highly eligible couple group has received an IUD and another 12 per cent has received conventional contraceptives.

The rate of insertion of IUD's has been most interesting. Attention is called to three features: (1) a rapid but short-lived (five months) increase in number of insertions starting about ten months after the first insertion; (2) an initial lag in insertions in residents outside Lulliani where no motivational program existed; and (3) a steady and rapid rise among these non-Lulliani residents until, by November, 1963, the number of insertions for such women exceeded those in Lulliani.

Because the national program is to concentrate its promotion on the IUD (in part through the use of mobile units), MESOREP has expanded its own IUD program and is covering villages near Lulliani. The three subcenters are being covered by weekly visits of the Lulliani health center lady doctor and two rural dispensaries are being visited by a pilot mobile IUD unit staffed by MESOREP independently from the health center. These extra Lulliani pilot studies began too recently for more than tentative data to be available now. The immediate effect was an approximate doubling of the number of insertions in March, with a subsequent fall off in April to the previous level. An interpretation immediately suggesting itself is that there was a backlog of women ready for insertions in the villages near Lulliani.

Insertions for residents of Lulliani have somewhat diminished, perhaps reflecting that a saturation point has been reached for the specific type of program to which Lulliani had been exposed.

One additional specific experiment in promotion of the IUD should be mentioned. In November, 1963, the *dais* (midwives) were offered Rs2 for each woman they brought to the health center who received an IUD. In a two-month period, seventy-eight payments were made. Preliminary thoughts on this experience are that the *dais* may be highly important in the promotion of the IUD, and a payment such as this may counteract their natural feeling of having their livelihood threatened by a family planning program.

Observation (Data Collection, Analysis, and Interpretation)

A final aspect of MESOREP, and an essential one for any scientific appraisal of its program, is that of data collection. Much time and money has gone into this aspect of the program in Lulliani. While this cannot be discussed adequately in this paper, a few words about it are in order.

Surveys have been conducted and routine service reporting and a registration system have been set up. The surveys have been of four types: (1) demographic, to provide background population data including birth, death, and migration rates. There have been three demographic surveys to date; (2) a socioeconomic survey to make possible the study of the association of behavior, knowledge, and attitudes with various social and economic variables; (3) a knowledge and attitude survey, which will be repeated, for information on status and changes in this area; (4) special interviews to investigate limited questions on selected groups, e.g., follow-up on mass meetings.

A special system for registering births, deaths, and migration has been established to augment and possibly improve upon the official registration system. This will assist in studies of the problem of assessing birth and death rates in rural Pakistan as well as contribute to the evaluation of the MESOREP program.

Miscellaneous

Much has been omitted from the above description of the MESOREP program. For example, no mention was made of the small trial of oral contraceptives in the village of Ali Raza Abad. There forty-five women have demonstrated that illiterate villagers can successfully use this method, synchronizing their taking of the pills with the phases of the moon.

The way in which a concentrated program can form a part of the existing health facilities of rural Pakistan is being studied. The tentative conclusions are encouraging for the IUD. Experience here obtained in problems of training, promotion, and distribution of contraceptives may have application beyond Pakistan, just as research and experience elsewhere have given aid and help to the Pakistani program.

4

Action Program of Family Planning in Puerto Rico

MANUEL E. PANIAGUA

To evaluate the contraceptive program of Puerto Rico in the proper perspective a brief review of this island's geographic, historic, socio-economic, and cultural background is first necessary.

Puerto Rico is a small tropical island of about 3,500 square miles in area (only 40 per cent of which is productive), very few natural resources, and over 2.5 million inhabitants. One-fourth of this population lives in the San Juan metropolitan area and about one-fifth in other cities and larger towns, while more than half is irregularly but quite thickly distributed throughout the rural areas, so that there is actually no place one can stand and not see at least some human dwelling. Most of the central part is very mountainous, and although the island is covered by a dense net of highways and roads, many of the rural dwellers must walk half a mile or more up and down the hillsides to reach these roads; they must then depend on an inefficient system of public transportation to go into town. On the other hand, electricity reaches nearly everywhere and most of the poorest people have access to radio.

During the four centuries of Spanish colonialism Puerto Rico led the quiet, sleepy life of most colonies living at the edge of the great historical movements, interrupted only occasionally by the attacks of other colonial powers at war with Spain and by the echoes of the liberating struggles in North and South America. An agricultural economy with a plantation system was developed very similar to that of the southern United States, complete with the importation of Negro slaves. The population grew gradually; during the nineteenth century it received the small addition of loyalist Spaniards expelled from their former homes and, later on, of political exiles from the neighboring republics, which changed regimes quite frequently. The latter are still coming in. By the turn of the twentieth century there were just under 1 million people; the majority is thoroughly mixed racially.

The slow rate of natural increase resulting from high birth and death rates began to give way during the early decades of the present century. Better sanitation and education and slightly improved nutrition reduce the death rate while the birth rate remained unchanged. During the past twenty years this process has been greatly accelerated by rising living standards and medical advances, so that, today, Puerto Rico is "threatened" by one of the lowest death rates in the world (6.5 per 1,000 population) and a rate of natural increase of 2.5 per cent per year.

Puerto Rican culture is nothing more than the original Spanish culture transplanted to the New World, modified by small doses of indigenous and African elements, and mollified by the tropical environment. As such it is very similar to that of the other Spanish-speaking countries around the Caribbean. The sexual morality of the majority of the people has been, until recently, definitely Victorian, hypocritical, and characterized by the double standard, with little or no communication between sexual partners. The majority also professes Roman Catholicism, liberally sprinkled with spiritualism, but is more superstitious than truly religious and does not let the stricter injunctions of the church interfere with the pursuit of pleasures or other interests (which is probably typical of most human societies).

There is, however, one notable difference between Puerto Rico and its neighbors: the close political and economic associations with the United States during the past sixty-five years have left a definite imprint. Probably the most important positive or beneficial effect of this association has been the integration into the Puerto Rican cultural pattern of such concepts as civil liberties, lay public education, and the separation of church and state.

The process of cultural Americanization has been accelerated as a result of urbanization, industrialization, and increased transportation and communication facilities between Puerto Rico and the mainland and has, in turn, generated a countercurrent of cultural nationalism, more marked during the last decade.

A very sketchy account of the birth control movement in Puerto Rico must start with Dr. Lanauze Rolón, a physician with a social conscience, who, in 1925, organized in Ponce, the second largest city, a League for Birth Control dedicated to the dissemination of information and open discussion of the population problem mostly as it affects individual indigent families. Pressure from the Catholic church and public indifference led to the disappearance of the League after a few years. Another similar movement was started in San Juan in 1932 by a group of civic-minded individuals who went as far as opening a clinic for contraceptive services, but again the pressure from the church and public apathy did away with it.

During the depression of the early nineteen-thirties, the Puerto Rican Reconstruction Administration (PRRA), a federal agency, was organized in an effort to help the economy, but very soon its directors realized that whatever economic gains their agency obtained were literally eaten up by the rapid population increase. In 1934 a maternal health program giving contraceptive advice was set up as part of the agency's program of medical services. Two years later, through the influence of the Catholic church in the U.S. government these services were eliminated. The same group of pioneers tried to continue offering contraceptive services under private auspices but met with little success.

It was not until 1937 that the local legislature, then controlled by the present opposition party, enacted some bills authorizing dissemination of birth control information and material and enabling the Secretary of Health to do so through government facilities. These bills were approved by the then Secretary of Agriculture and acting Governor (and now President of the Puerto Rico Family Planning Association), Mr. Rafael Menéndez-Ramos, against the opposition of the Catholic church and some segments of society. The Secretary of Health immediately started a widespread contraceptive program, but, in the 1940 election his party was defeated for reasons that had nothing to do with this program; the new incumbent, the present Resident Commissioner of Puerto Rico in Congress, was opposed to the program and under him and his successor it was allowed to wither away.

In the meantime, the economic expansion brought about by World War II and the postwar boom were coupled with a program of social justice by the Popular Party that resulted in a gradual rising of the extremely low living standard. The hope of improvement stirred the beginning of motivation for family limitation, but the methods of temporary contraception available then were too complicated for constant and correct use by people of low motivation and low educational level. Furthermore, the pattern for almost everyone was to think about family limitation only after there were too many children, so surgical sterilization became the most popular method of contraception.

In 1946 a two-day forum on the population problem was held in San Juan with the participation, among other civic and intellectual leaders, of the then President of the Senate, Mr. Muñoz Marín, and the director of Operation Bootstrap, Teodoro Moscoso. As a result of the enthusiasm generated there, a group of participants organized the Association for Population Studies, which, for the next ten years, worked hard at gathering, interpreting, and disseminating data on the population problem and on urging the community to plan some action.

During the late forties and early fifties, as the popular demand for contraception (mainly female sterilization) increased, the services supplied by the Department of Health, on which 80 per cent of the population depends, tended to decrease for several reasons. First, there was a lack of positive leadership by the government, which has maintained a neutral policy toward contraception, supplying the services if and when requested at the premises and if the local physician is willing. At the same time, many economists were taken in by the remarkable improvement made possible, in spite of the high rate of natural increase in population, by the continuous flow of emigration to the U.S.

Almost as important has been the increasing effectiveness of Catholic church opposition. Unable to persuade the vast majority of Puerto Rican women not to use contraception, except the rhythm method, the church concentrated its efforts on those who supplied the services. Indoctrination courses for physicians, nurses, social workers, and government and civic leaders were quite successful. This was typical of the tendency to conservatism and conformism that is found in most improving economies. The overcrowding of public schools led to an expansion of the parochial school system, which is overwhelmingly Catholic, and through the children the clergy was able to influence the parents. All these factors have contributed to make active, church-going Catholicism a status symbol.

Because of the weakening of the movement, the Association for Population Studies decided to shift its emphasis to an action program. In 1956 it changed its name to the Puerto Rico Family Planning Association, became affiliated with the International Planned Parenthood Federation, and launched a research program on oral contraceptives in collaboration with the Worcester Foundation for Experimental Biology, Shrewsbury, Mass. The Association could not embark on a widespread education and service program, however, until 1957, when Mr. Joseph Sunnen of St. Louis, Mo., through the Sunnen Foundation, began underwriting these operations. Mr. Sunnen's purpose was to help get the program started and finance it for a few years until the government would take over the main burden of direct services and local philanthropy would support the rest of the activities. His criterion for success would be a sharp decline in the crude birth rate.

It was soon discovered that direct services through the usual clinic set-up could not reach the majority of women who needed them most. The approach was changed; instead of waiting for motivated persons to seek the service by attending a clinic, a system was organized to provide the simplest services in the homes, fields, and factories. This system was the brainchild of the Executive Director of the Association, Mrs. Celestina Zalduondo, who brought to the position her fifteen-year experience directing the Division of Public Welfare of the Department of Health, her boundless energy, and a true dedication to the program.

During the first two years several systems were tried unsuccessfully. Finally, in 1959, it was decided to combine the use of volunteers with that of full-time paid employees. Taking into consideration the topographic and population characteristics mentioned above, the island was divided into twenty areas, each comprising three or four towns with their corresponding rural areas; the capital was to be served directly from the main office. A resident of one of the towns was chosen as area supervisor and given the task of organizing and co-ordinating both the educational and the direct services aspects of the program. To help him or her carry out this task the supervisor would try to enlist the help of civic-minded individuals already cognizant of the problem and sympathetic to the program, such as the mayor, the school superintendent or principal, labor leaders, the Protestant minister, some school teachers, and other leaders of the community. Wherever feasible, a local chapter of the Association was organized; if not, these people would assist the supervisor unofficially upon request.

The supervisor then proceeded to canvass every village, hamlet, or community in the area and seek any volunteers who were well known and respected, interested in helping their neighbors, and brave enough to withstand criticism. These volunteers were instructed by the supervisor so that they in turn might transmit the message to their neighbors; at the same time, these volunteers were also given the task of storing the contraceptive material.

A small office was set up in the largest town of each area where the supervisor would devote one day a week to office work, contraceptive distribution, and to processing requests for assistance in obtaining sterilization (still one of the most popular methods of contraception), as well as requests for educational services. The other four days were devoted to field work, one day in each municipality of the area. Education went hand in hand with the service program. The supervisor would also organize panel discussions and meetings, lectures, film exhibitions, and all the usual activities.

The use of volunteer leaders proved to be a very wise choice. For one thing, it allowed extensive coverage which would have been impossible on an exclusively professional basis, since the contribution of the Sunnen Foundation, though very generous, was not limitless. More important still, there was better acceptance of both the idea of contraception and the method to be practiced when the matter was presented by a friend or relative well acquainted with the subject's individual problems rather than by an official of the Health Department or of a private agency. Furthermore, the accessibility to the contraceptive material made its continuous use much easier.

This whole system was, of course, predicated upon the availability of some very simple, acceptable contraceptive which would not require medical or paramedical supervision. Fortunately, by the time the distribution system was organized, Sunnen had developed an aerosol foam contraceptive which was supplied free for this program. Although this material was offered first by the volunteer leaders and given free if wanted, potential customers had a choice of any of the accepted methods if they were willing to pay the same wholesale prices that the Association had paid for them and if they made their requests at the town office.

The success of the system of distribution, as distinguished from the contraceptive program as a whole, can be judged by the fact that despite the strident and sometimes slanderous opposition of the Catholic church and its satellite organizations, three years after its inception, 1,500 volunteer leaders were supplying contraceptive instruction and materials to about 30,000 couples. It is estimated that since the beginning of the program about 100,000 persons have been instructed in the use of contraceptives and given some material.

During the same period, a total of 9,912 sterilizations (7,017 female, 2,895 male) have been performed under the auspices of the Association.

The results obtained varied with the ability and dedication of the area supervisor and the volunteers and the circumstances of each particular community. The importance of the latter is demonstrated by the varying degree of success accomplished in different towns within the same area. The attitudes of the municipal officials, the school personnel, the public health people, and, most important, the intensity of activity of the local Catholic hierarchy and laity have all had an effect on the program.

The municipal authorities, especially the mayors, have been in a particularly uncomfortable position. They and their party workers are familiar with the problems of their constituents and are usually under some pressure from them to provide contraceptive services (again, mostly sterilization), but, on the other hand, they are confronted with the attacks of the Catholic church and related organizations to which belong many of the leaders of the community. At the same time, the Commonwealth government, on which the mayors rely for orientation and help, continues its policy of passive neutrality. The majority of the mayors are courageous enough to voice their convictions and are favorable to the program; many of them collaborate to the extent of allowing the Association to set up its office, rent free, in an empty room of the town hall, much to the annoyance of the local priest.

Both the school and the health people, who in Puerto Rico are controlled by the Commonwealth and not by the municipal government, are relatively free from political pressures but not from social pressures or those exerted by the Catholic church over them or their superiors. They are for or against the program on a more personal basis, depending on how much of a social conscience they have developed.

The opposition of the Catholic church and its front organizations has taken different forms and has varied in intensity and effectiveness. All kinds of pressure have been brought to bear, mainly on the community leaders, including the volunteers and even some area supervisors.

In general, it may be said that the program has been least successful in the towns and villages of the mountainous interior where rural conditions predominate, educational levels are lowest, and the hold of the Catholic church over the people is strongest.

The attitude of the Commonwealth government toward contracep-

tion is worth analyzing even at the risk of oversimplification. During
the past twenty-four years the present Governor, Mr. Muñoz Marín,
has literally led the people of Puerto Rico out of the wilderness of
extreme poverty, economic stagnation, and utter despair. He has made
use of all the resources made available to him by luck or circumstance,
but, when necessary, he has himself created these favorable circumstances. The people have become accustomed to his leadership to the
extent that Puerto Rico's is a one-man government. At this very
moment Muñoz is having difficulty trying to divest himself from some
of the political power that has been concentrated in his hands, in
preparation for a possible succession.

During the late nineteen-fifties, and coinciding with activation of the
Puerto Rico Family Planning Association, the Catholic church stepped
up its campaign of indoctrination, concentrating more on high government officials and political leaders of diverse coloration. It went as far
as falsely accusing the government of advocating birth control. Early in
1960, a well-organized mass demonstration of Catholics marched on
the capitol and demanded from the Legislature the abolition of the
laws allowing contraception as well as the approval of release time
from public schools for religious instruction.

Having failed to intimidate the Legislature, these activists proceeded to organize a Christian Action Party, which other Christian
churches, though invited, refused to join. It was only a few months
before the election that the local Catholic bishops, in their famous
pastoral letters, implicitly threatened their flocks with eternal damna-
tion if they voted for the Popular Party. The reaction was immediate.
Muñoz, master politician that he is, turned the tables on the bishops by
stating that there was no incompatibility between being a good
Catholic and a good "popular" but that the bishops could err as human
beings. The party leadership remained faithful to him and, in an effort to emphasize his position, many of them made public displays of
piety and church-going.

After having defeated the Catholic Action Party in the election and
after a postelectoral legislative investigation had demonstrated that the
party created to bring morality to Puerto Rico had committed widespread fraud during registration, Muñoz was only too ready to be
conciliated by the church and to avoid further unpleasantness. The
church made use of some of its most loyal members among his advisers
to make an approach, and during the past few years, there has been a

progressive rapprochement, which has resulted in the encroachment of the church into areas that should remain outside of its jurisdiction.

Much has been accomplished during the past seven years, though not necessarily what Mr. Sunnen had in mind when he so generously started his contribution.

1. The experience acquired has made possible the articulation of a set of principles (which will be enumerated later) for the successful establishment of action programs in Puerto Rico or in other countries of similar cultural background.

2. The mere fact that the program has been carried out has destroyed the myth that it was impossible to do anything about contraception in a "Catholic" country.

3. The education program plus the public controversy with the Catholic church and the consequent publicity have kept the movement in the headlines and the people constantly aware of the problem.

4. It has indirectly helped the self-supporting research programs by providing a congenial environment and the backing of a well-known organization.

On the other hand, the program has failed to coax the government into facing up to its responsibility of taking the initiative in supplying contraceptive services to the medically indigent. On the contrary, wherever the program was very active the Public Health unit shifted to the Association the burden of giving contraceptive services by the simple expedient of referring the applicants directly.

The program has also failed to obtain substantial help from local philanthropy. This is understandable since there are very few rich people in Puerto Rico (and most of these are Catholic) and since there is no tradition of philanthropy. Some who are more or less sympathetic to the cause are afraid of the publicity they might receive. They could give anonymously, of course, but that would probably take away the main satisfaction derived from giving.

During the past seven years the crude birth rate has decreased from 34.9 to 30.5, a very small drop which is further reduced when adjusted for changes in the age structure of the population. Most of this decrease is attributed by demographers to the emigration of younger people of the reproductive age and the temporary disruption of some marriages.

What will happen in the near future in the contraceptive field is anybody's guess. Will the government assume a more positive attitude now that net emigration has practically stopped and unemployment is rising? Will the more tolerant stand of the so-called liberal segment of the Catholic hierarchy diffuse to Puerto Rico? What will be the position of the Catholic independents who are at present dead set against any form of population control on the grounds that it is national suicide? The answers to all these questions would necessarily be highly speculative and would fall outside the scope of this presentation.

The experience acquired during these years has led to the formulation of the following principles for the organization and functioning of contraceptive programs:

1. Every program must be adapted to the cultural, socioeconomic, geographic, and technological peculiarities of each country, region, or community.

2. An intensive educational program should precede and accompany any form of service program.

3. Because of the magnitude of the task, the government of the particular community, region, or country is best equipped to handle such programs. The services should be integrated into the educational, health, preventive, and welfare measures, although it may be wise to have some board or committee to integrate the various phases of the program that come under different government agencies.

In countries where there is political instability it may be preferable that the program be administered by an autonomous, subsidized institution which is as free from partisan politics as possible.

In any case, it is necessary to have some private institution to act as a trail-blazer in orientation and research and to serve as watchdog over the public or semipublic agencies which supply the services and, whenever necessary, to reinforce them.

4. The success of any contraceptive program depends first on the degree of motivation of the people and second on the acceptability of the methods available. It is, therefore, imperative that a service program provide a wide variety of contraceptive methods and devices, including sterilization. It is also necessary that service be provided both in the usual clinics and in the homes, depending on the circumstances and the type of contraceptive chosen.

5. The educational program should start emphasizing those areas where there is most agreement, so as to avoid controversy and not to antagonize people unnecessarily. From the very beginning it should try to involve all segments of society in family planning. In Latin America

in particular, where the male usually has the decisive voice in most things concerning the family, it is very important to gain his approval and bring him into the picture. Wherever there is a strong, organized opposition, as in most places dominated by the Roman Catholic church, controversy may be unavoidable, but it is important to ignore the abuse and maintain a calm but firm stand in defense of the rights of the individual to decide for himself whether or not he wants to avail himself of the services offered.

6. If there are not enough technical or financial resources to start a program throughout a large area, it is preferable to concentrate in a few well-chosen zones where the population is most receptive and the need for the services is greatest.

7. Periodic evaluation of the program for the purpose of readjustment is mandatory. New contraceptive techniques are being developed continuously; sociological research into attitudes and motivations is forcing revision of stereotyped ideas; increasing communication is bringing about cultural interchanges. All this intellectual ferment raises the hope that man may be at last using his brains in the effort to solve his problems.

5

Discussion of Papers 1–4

CARL E. TAYLOR

TAYLOR: I liked the preceding papers because of their frank recognition of the major problems that we face. On the other hand, we also must try not to make the solutions sound too mysterious.

Dr. Freymann mainly discussed the future plans in India based on what has been learned so far. I would like to ask him to give us his estimate of the rank order of the specific motivational factors that have been identified in the work in India and especially about the relative importance of family economics. Dr. Sadik made the point that the family's concern about their economic status seems to be a dominating consideration in Pakistan. Similarly, I was much interested in Dr. Paniagua's statement that the growing conservatism in Puerto Rico is interfering with acceptance of family planning and that this conservatism seems to be increasing as economic development occurs.

I would like to present a simple conceptual model on the relationship between family economics and the acceptability of family planning (Figure 1). It is based on the possibility that we are dealing with a threshold effect. The first threshold is the minimum subsistence level, or more specifically, the family's concept of minimum subsistence. The response to a family planning program is probably good with the acceptance of family planning rising rather rapidly below this subsistence level. At this point there is probably a leveling off, as economic conditions improve, until we come to a second threshold, which is the point at which family affluence and wants increase so that they begin to choose between children and some other things, especially some kind of material purchase, such as a bicycle. Beyond this second threshold, we may expect to see steady and progressive increase in the acceptability of family planning. My main evidence for this model is our experience in the Ludhiana studies in India, where rather than a

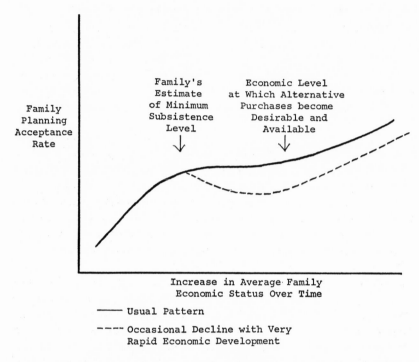

Figure 1. Conceptual model of relationship between family economics and acceptance of family planning.

leveling off between the two thresholds there seemed to be an actual decline. In the early nineteen-fifties when the project started, general willingness to accept family planning seemed greater than in 1960, and the villagers themselves spoke of this change as being related to better economic opportunities.

My question to Dr. Sadik relates to a very basic issue that is frequently raised about the relative usefulness of health services as the major base for family planning programs. Possible alternatives are other types of government services, such as community development. According to these four papers, it seems that we can choose among many alternatives. In India, on the one hand, the emphasis is being placed largely on providing additional family planning resources and personnel as part of the general health program. In Puerto Rico, for political reasons, they have had to work outside of the government health services with a separate voluntary organization. Pakistan does not yet have health services available on a mass scale in the villages, but will have to develop something *de novo;* the pertinent question is: in which direction does Pakistan expect to move?

And a minor question to Dr. Rider: Do you have any estimate at this point about the impact that the intra-uterine device program is having on the birth rate? If a plateau is appearing in the acceptance of this device at Lulliani, is it coming at a point where there is any reason to expect an effect on the birth rate? Or is the plateau merely what we have seen in a good many other places where the introduction of a new device is followed by a wave of initial acceptance which is due to substitution of a more convenient method for other methods that were already being used?

CHAIRMAN STEBBINS: Thank you, Dr. Taylor. First, Dr. Freymann, would you answer the question on the rank order?

FREYMANN: On the basis of survey findings in the Indian population, when men are asked about possible reasons for accepting family planning, economic motivations and justifications are predominantly mentioned. When women are asked, health reasons are given.

I am not sure, however, that the correct model is a completely rational one in which people judge values and make a decision. I suspect some of the value associations are latent, and perhaps one of the most important things which remains unsaid in these survey situations is what you might call fashion or the group norm. The innovators probably do judge these things rationally, but I suspect that most people, given a certain set of conditions, follow the norm once it is accepted by the group and is the fashionable thing to do and then adjust afterward.

With regard to Dr. Taylor's model, there is a study from the Indian Statistical Institute in which they observe relationships between the subsistence level and the fertility rate. Also, there is an interesting relevant finding in the New Delhi population on this same question of economic level and the birth rate. According to these surveys, economic matters definitely influence fertility. There is evidence, even in the lower economic group, that after a certain number of children, people do something about family limitation. But, in general, the higher the economic level, the sooner the practice of family limitation is initiated.

CALVER: Mr. Chairman, may I ask Dr. Freymann which is the effect and which is the cause? It might be that they have more money because they have less children, and the speaker seems to indicate that they have less children because they have more money, if I understand it correctly.

HILL: Mr. Chairman, I think that there is pretty clear evidence that down at the lowest end of the socioeconomic scale the former factor works, that is, having more money permits them to have more children, but at the upper end of the scale, I think it does not.

MENDOZA: My experience after World War II working with displaced persons from every country in the world and from every cultural background in the same economic status was that the people who had higher education knew how to do something about controlling their fertility, but that those who were in the lower educational level, regardless of their cultural background, were the ones who reproduced themselves irresponsibly.

CHAIRMAN STEBBINS: There was a question also to you, Dr. Sadik. Would you answer?

SADIK: I have this document on how we hope to use other services to assist in family planning, and we have listed all the organizations that we will use in our Third Five Year Plan. It is divided into a short-term policy and a long-term program. We feel that we cannot keep up a short-term program forever and make this a part of the way of life. We have put emphasis on future generations and are trying to introduce the concept of the small family into our educational system. The school boards are rewriting primary readers to introduce the advantage of a small family.

If we had someone from the Department of Information and Broadcasting who was trained in the techniques of motivation or communication, perhaps we would do a better job than is being done by the Health Ministry, which is in charge of producing films and posters and other things that are to be used in family planning education.

Doctors are not really trained for this or for a lot of other things they are supposed to do in family planning. They do not know how to set up a distributing system. Neither do they know enough of economics, commerce, education, and broadcasting. We have a Ministry of Law working out regulations, and we feel it would be a good thing to have its co-operation too. We want the Ministry of Labor to co-operate with us because big industrial organizations can be of great help.

The armed forces are a very well-organized unit which can also be incorporated in the program. The hospitals, dispensaries, and all the professional people in the private sector must be tapped. They do not know anything about the family planning program and do not want to do anything about it. We do have quite a number of private practitioners, and if we tell them family planning is a national service and could induce them to do something actively, like perform sterilizations, perhaps they will aid us. We have a Basic Democractic system in which one Basic Democrat represents 1,000 or 1,500 people. They are spread throughout the country. They are elected by the people in the villages, and if we can get all the basic democracies and their local leaders to co-operate with the program, we may be able to get a lot of help from them.

In fact, I feel that the program is very little of a health problem; it is more a problem of social change. We have to convince the people that all the things they have believed in for so many generations are now changed or changing and that a small family is the right answer to all of the problems that we have. In connection with this, we have a rural experiment going on where acceptance of family planning immediately decreased with increased economy. As soon as the economic status increased, the number of people coming for family planning advice immediately decreased. The people told us that now they were better off and had more food and could feed the additional children.

So, I would say that Dr. Taylor's model is probably correct and that it will take some time for the people we are discussing to realize that they can buy something else in place of a child.

CHAIRMAN STEBBINS: Thank you, Dr. Sadik. Would you like to comment now, Dr. Rider?

RIDER: Let me review Dr. Taylor's question first to make sure I understand it. It was a double-barreled question involving the inquiry whether the apparent plateau in the insertion rate at Lulliani attained a sufficient level to produce a decline in the birth rate and, secondly, whether we are dealing with a substitution of one device by individuals who had been users of other devices. We do not really have data available yet to answer those questions precisely. However, I have some information that particularly bears on the second point.

We have data regarding the use of conventional types of contraception, and one of the leading features of those data is that our clientele very seldom come back for more supplies. Even though the intrauterine device may be a substitution in the literal sense that they have tried contraception before and now are taking up a new device, it seems very likely that it is considered to be an improvement, not just substituting one thing for another. As to the exact level and its effect, I can only point out that it is at present approximately 10 per cent of the current highly eligible couples that are using it.

Dr. Sheps has developed interesting mathematical models to help study the effect of different acceptance rates, and I await with interest the gathering of data from our study to answer such questions in more detail through identification of the users and their previous history.

CHAIRMAN STEBBINS: The papers are now open for general discussion. Questions, comments? Dr. Paniagua?

PANIAGUA: The discussion leader did not put a question to me, but I would like to clarify one point. When I mentioned conformism and conservatism, I was referring to them indirectly in relation to church attendance.

As you know, church-going or religious activity of any kind is a form of conformism. Since a majority of the Puerto Ricans is Catholic, the majority of the people are going to attend Catholic churches and be influenced by the Catholic church, and this would indirectly affect the program.

POLGAR: I want to ask Dr. Freymann if he would comment on the question Dr. Taylor asked Dr. Sadik: namely, under the new system, what is going to be the tie-up between the hierarchy you mentioned and the Ministry of Health personnel in India?

FREYMANN: The new organization for family planning in India is grafted onto the health structure and at its local level is attached to the District Health Officer or to the Block health unit.

The role of a particular group of family planning workers, for example, is so defined that they should spend most of their time mobilizing the contributions of the community development workers at the Block level so that they participate in the family planning program. It has been demonstrated that unless you have a full-time worker at this level, you cannot mobilize the contribution of people in other agencies. The Block unit is a fairly homogenous unit and oftentimes the headquarters are together and there are good opportunities for interchange and co-operation between various agencies at this level.

PEASE: Is the family planning budget within the budget of the Ministry of Health or within the State Ministry?

FREYMANN: All the expenses chargeable to family planning are reimbursed to the state government by the Central Grants Committee.

SEGAL: I would like to point out that a very attractive aspect of the organizational structure in India is that it establishes the basic administrative framework into which any new methodology that might be developed can fit without having to regear the entire program. There is a great deal of flexibility at the lower levels, the levels actually working with villagers, so that the opportunity to make fine adjustments depending upon methods that might be evolved in the near future does exist.

Now, I would like to ask Dr. Freymann two questions. To what extent is there a likelihood that the decentralization of health services in different states in India, from the state level down to the local village group level, might influence the ability of the state health services actually to implement this kind of staffing? Also, do we know that the reason that the higher parity is continued in the lower economic class is related to failure to use the methods that are available to them, failure to use them successfully, or failure to accept any methodology at all?

FREYMANN: I will try to answer your second question and then refer the first one to Dr. Rao or Dr. Leavell.

The dynamics are not all together known, but in the upper economic group you find many people using a variety of methods, including sterilization and abortion. In the lower economic group you find people not practicing contraception at all. An interesting facet of this is that some observations have been made on the pattern of visits of the family planning workers who are nice middle-class girls: they spend most of their time visiting upper-class couples and are very uncomfortable with lower-class couples.

RAO: The question raised by Dr. Segal with regard to actual implementation of the program at the village level is very important. As Dr. Freymann has stated, there is a family planning medical officer who is to supervise the local workers. At the Block level (there are about 5,500 Blocks) the medical officer is expected to supervise the work of the nurses. With the new pattern it is suggested that a health worker will attend not only to family planning work but also to health education. Also, there are some women working locally who have been interested in the additional work of family planning and population problems. It is important that the social educational organizations and the women's movement become involved in the program. But generally there is widespread acceptance of the program except in certain areas where there are political problems that, owing to the distribution of seats in the legislature, come in the way of the national program being accepted.

The recent Chinese invasion of India has also upset the general public opinion as to the acceptance of this program because we always talked about numbers; with 700 million people marching on the northern frontier, people began wondering why they should reduce their population.

I would like to make a general observation on the question of population control in India. The per capita income is very low. The literacy is low. Basic health services are limited. In family planning, when we get to the question of motivation, the problem of disseminating knowledge, of communication, has been one of our main difficulties.

The great advances in technology with regard to the new methods of contraception should be very helpful. The techniques will be explained to small groups and at mass meetings with mixed audiences. It is already having a good effect rather than an effect that would depreciate our family planning program. In any event, we believe that this new way of life, the habit of birth control, has to be integrated with the social and economic process both in the field of education as well as the general welfare because, unless there are opportunities for women to educate themselves, it is very unlikely that we will have woman personnel available for health services. Therefore, it is our aim to see not only that there is education but also that women are given opportunities to have free secondary school education.

There is one other point which I wish to emphasize: The Ministry of Health thought that family planning should be integrated with their services because the emphasis of the program is to be on the mother's health. The communicable disease control program and the preservation of as many children as possible are also being taken up. We are planning to go into some of the questions of how we may get across the knowledge of family planning to the people simultaneously with the promotion of other control programs.

The other problem is the one related to techniques of contraception. Apparently, anything that is to be suggested must be simple and at the same time acceptable both to the husband and the wife.

It is the policy of the Indian government to request international agencies to help with the organization of family planning and with the supply and distribution of contraceptives, so that the distribution may be both from the public agencies of the general health services and also from various voluntary organizations. Whenever a country likes to help a developing country it should not make much distinction between the public sector and the private sector. We are very happy that the Ford Foundation has invited people to discuss the manufacture of contraceptives in India. I do hope the government will be permitted to handle this matter because of the importance of making chemical contraceptives available to the people. If the supplies are not available, there will be frustration and lack of interest. It is something that has to continue for a long time because India is not an advanced country. Therefore, it is necessary that these manufacturers should be in the public sector, though, at the same time, local private manufacturers may have to be encouraged.

The evaluation program is very important. As Dr. Freymann has mentioned, the work is being closely observed both at the centers and in various districts where family planning is being introduced. But ultimately the general health services will have to help considerably in the expansion of this evaluation program. When the Ford Foundation came forward to encourage family planning, they thought it important to improve the general health services, and they therefore are helping us in the organization of an institute responsible for general health services.

CHAIRMAN STEBBINS: Thank you very much, Dr. Rao. Dr. Berman, would you like to comment?

BERMAN: I just want to comment on Dr. Paniagua's statement in reference to the Catholic church; in contradistinction to Puerto Rico, there is an entirely different attitude in Latin America in relation to the church's participation in this type of program. As the Latin Americans say, the church there has a considerable degree of autonomy under the Holy See. I think this changing attitude is amazing in that they want to study their problem and they want to train workers and to experiment with various new developments.

They are certainly cognizant of their tremendous abortion problems and of the illegitimacy problems which affect the moral structure of the church. The bishops in Latin America do have great autonomy, and many of them either have instituted or permitted certain types of birth control.

I think that one of the basic problems in Latin America is to observe closely the changing attitude and to determine which methods are acceptable to government, church, and private groups.

COOK: My question deals with the production of condoms in India, which appears to have ceased. There was a factory set up under the planning authorities to manufacture condoms, but they were not able to produce any condoms and have closed up their shop. The report says that condom production in India is back where it was a decade ago. What is the basis for this rather curious situation?

CHAIRMAN STEBBINS: Who wants to answer this?

FREYMANN: Which factory do you refer to?

COOK: The Associated Rubber Industries, an Indian group and a British company.

FREYMANN: They had a limited production for a while and the product was not accepted by the government of India. It was defective. They had no alternative. It was a very small fly-by-night operation. The only considerable production now in view in India is with the London Rubber Company and a company called Seymour's Limited; they will start producing probably the end of this year.

CHAIRMAN STEBBINS: Dr. Baumgartner?

BAUMGARTNER: I want to point out another recent change: that is that the British Technical Operation Services, which are the equivalent of the AID of the U.S. and the American services are now willing and eager to give technical assistance in this field. They are also willing to assist, if necessary, in the manufacturing field, though they doubt if it is necessary because they think the country's own companies can handle this on private capital, and they do not have quite so much of the exchange problem. Certainly the British and the Japanese companies are interested in expansion on a commercial basis. I think that help may be obtained on the commercial side as well as on the technical assistance side. It is my impression that the Japanese have a little more trouble language-wise than the British do, but, at any rate, they are waiting for requests for help.

CHAIRMAN STEBBINS: Dr. Taylor?

TAYLOR: May I just comment once more about the model (Figure 1) I presented. I am pleased with the fact that there is evidence supporting the model because all of us who are concerned with this area have been criticized for so long by the development economists that it would be very nice for us to be able to show that the economists are to blame for some of the problems of population growth. If it can be shown over a time scale that the economic development in itself is contributing to the population problem, then it would relieve some of the pressures on us.

BAUMGARTNER: Are we after just having fewer children or just economic development? Aren't these pretty short-term things? Do we really care so long as there is a balance between the national resources of the country and the peoples' ability to use them and the numbers of people? I think this is a small thing. We can get ourselves in another box here if we look at these things as separate objectives.

TAYLOR: It seems to me that this is a very important point because it is a stage in our understanding of the relationship between family economics and general economics. The family's appreciation of their own economic situation as it relates to the more latent drives and values which they have carried with them into a situation where their economic change occurs is a matter of great significance. So I think what we need to understand is the relationship between the general pictures at this point, and I thought this sort of model might help us to do that.

BAUMGARTNER: The other question I would have asked about this is: "Are there really things to buy that are readily available so that there is some choice?" In many places we act as if this is a simple factor. My hunch is that if you got a few Sears and Roebuck stores out there with a lot of gadgets as well as a lot of good contraceptives, you might have a different picture.

MENDOZA: The important difference between Puerto Rico and the rest of the Latin American countries is that the Latin American countries are just beginning the family planning movement. It is a matter of only two-and-a-half or three years since we started working in Latin America in family planning. Puerto Rico was the first Catholic country to do the work, so there is a tremendous difference in its attitude to this matter.

In Latin America, everyone is trying to work with the church. They invite the Father to speak and bless them when they have the first family planning meeting. Every group tries not to antagonize the church but to work with it. Everybody agrees that there is a crucial need for the regulation of births, but when the question comes to methods, nobody knows what happens between the doctor and the patient.

PANIAGUA: At the risk of overdoing it, there are a couple of things with this church aspect that I would like to mention besides what Dr. Mendoza said about the difference between Puerto Rico and Latin America. Dr. Berman gave us a very nice résumé of his recent experience in Latin America; at the meeting in Puerto Rico, we were very surprised about the progress they were making. Maybe the

Catholic church is moving a little faster, but there is another reason why I feel that there is such a difference between the attitudes of the church in Puerto Rico and in the rest of Latin America.

We are talking about the Catholic church, but the Catholic church is no more monolithical than the Communist Party. Actually, there is a great difference in Puerto Rico between what the high hierarchy and the more educated bishops think and what many parish priests or Catholic laymen do about this problem. Dr. Berman, I understand that you visited mainly with the princes of the Church and maybe an occasional bishop, but you may find their attitude in Latin America much different than that of the local priest.

BERMAN: I did not have time for wide sampling of opinion, so I went to the top. But in essence, I think that the change in attitude with each cardinal or archbishop that I met was due to the social science advisers with him. I found these people were the most liberal philosophically that you could ever meet. There are certain church forces at work in Latin America today that are interested in a population center for all of Latin America, and this is the liberal wing of both the hierarchy and the social science department of the church.

PANIAGUA: That is what we hope will come to Puerto Rico.

PEASE: This seems particularly interesting in view of the fact that I think historically the Catholic church in Latin America has been very conservative. It is very hard for me to believe that (and I have been involved in Latin America for three or four years) there has been any drastic change in the last couple of years except that we are beginning to get the first breakthrough, as Dr. Mendoza pointed out. But we have still got a long way to go, and although what Dr. Berman has said gives us optimism for the future, I would say it is a bit too optimistic.

MENDOZA: We should also note that the church has been very conservative and has been joined with the powerful economic groups in Latin America who are the landholders. But the Catholic church is now changing very rapidly and trying to do as much as possible to help the masses in their pursuit of social and economic advance. This whole idea applies even with family planning.

6

Action Programs of Family Planning in Japan

MINORU MURAMATSU

Some of the most important aspects of the various action programs in the field of family planning and fertility control which have been conducted after the war in Japan, mainly by the government but partially by voluntary organizations, are summarized in the first half of this paper.

Government-Sponsored Programs

Immediately after the war, in 1947 and 1948, Japan experienced a sudden and sharp increase in her population as a result of large-scale demobilization and repatriation and the resultant upsurge in births. A total of nearly 80 million people then had to live on the greatly reduced land areas available, and the problems of overpopulation were apparent everywhere, especially in cities. Confronted with serious difficulties in their daily life, people soon started to try to avoid births, or at least to postpone them, in order not to lower further their level of living. The major method employed for this purpose in those years was induced abortion. The total incidence of induced abortion was undoubtedly fairly high even before the enactment of the Eugenic Protection Law in 1948, but, in any event, the increasingly widespread use of this practice became manifest as revealed by the annual number of induced abortions reported to the health authorities under the Law since then.

Recognizing the acute demand for fertility control and that, to an

67

alarming degree, induced abortion had become a major means, the then Japanese government discussed the matter seriously and agreed upon issuing a special statement, in the form of a cabinet decision, on October 26, 1951. The statement, widely publicized in newspapers, read in part: "The number of induced abortions is increasing each year. These are often necessary to protect the life and health of the mother. Occasional damage to the mother's health, however, makes the dissemination of the knowledge of contraception desirable to eliminate the bad influence of abortions on the mother's health. . . ."

In response to this cabinet decision of October, 1951, which aimed to promote conception control primarily from the standpoint of maternal health protection, a specific "plan to promote conception control" was compiled by the Ministry of Health and Welfare and sent to all prefectural governors in June, 1952. This document is monumental in the sense that it provided, for the first time, a definite official basis whereby the government agencies of public health and welfare could actually participate in the programs of family planning promotion.

In this plan, three levels of family planning education of the general public were suggested: "general education" in the principles of family planning; "group education," designed to assist small groups of people in learning about various techniques in general; and "individual education," which affords an opportunity for a detailed personal consultation about contraception with an instructor. For the general educational approach, central and prefectural public health agencies were given responsibilities, while the other two approaches were to be undertaken by local health centers. A great many directives regarding these programs were issued by the central and prefectural agencies to local health centers, audio-visual educational material was produced and used extensively, and family planning meetings and conferences were held in many parts of the country.

As time went on, however, evaluation revealed certain defects of these government-sponsored programs. In general, the efforts to disseminate basic information about family planning through "general" or "group" education seemed fairly successful. On the other hand, the "individual" education conducted at the local health center proved unsuccessful, despite the fact that family planning was such an interesting subject to the local people.

From these observations, several important points were brought to the attention of the family planning experts concerned: (1) The Japanese people as a whole had been keenly interested in family planning in the first place. A fundamental reason for the seemingly high degree of success in the efforts of general education of family planning conducted by the government was this "pre-existence" of interest in the subject and the resultant ready acceptance of it. (2) However, this readiness did not necessarily deny entirely the value of the programs sponsored by the government. The real value of these programs, so far as the Japanese experience was concerned, was that the positive attitude on the part of the government, which still retained a great amount of authority, gave powerful support, assurance, and encouragement to the people's interest in family planning. Once people were assured that their thought and behavior had been endorsed by the government, family planning could easily be talked about and practiced. (3) In spite of such a favorable atmosphere and the keen interest in the subject, many persons were embarrassd to seek assistance because of the highly personal aspects of contraception. Few women were courageous enough to come to a health center to see an instructor whose duty was the teaching of contraceptive techniques. Furthermore, the authority which the government carried acted as an obstacle in this case. A health center, which was a part of the government, had an "official" atmosphere which made it difficult for a woman to talk about her private life. Failure in the efforts of the individual consultation services at the health centers, therefore, was indicative of the need for family planning workers to go out and see the people in their homes, not of the absence of interest in such a service of the people.

Reviewing these defects and shortcomings, a shift in the strategy of family planning promotion has gradually been enacted by the government since around 1960. Schemes primarily designed for general enlightenment gave way to more specific programs of personal consultation. Training programs in the teaching of contraception were conducted extensively throughout the country in order to qualify local midwives as conception control instructors, since the use of midwives for this purpose was considered advisable, particularly in view of their wide geographical distribution. At present, there are some 40,000 midwives thus trained for a population of about 97 million, and about one-quarter of these have been specifically assigned to help indigent people in matters of family planning and contraception, for which service a small honorarium is paid to them by the government. At the same time, the administration of family planning programs has been transferred from health centers to local community authorities, such as town or village offices, with a view to securing closer involvement of the total community in the programs. Today there are about 1,000 communities in Japan which have been enough interested in family planning to conduct their own programs for its promotion, and local women's associations, 4-H clubs, farmers' co-operatives, PTA's, and so on have been providing helpful assistance in these communities. In nearly 300 villages and towns, moreover, the so-called maternal and child health centers have been established where contraceptive advice is given by midwives and public health nurses to women along with other prenatal and postnatal consultations.

Thus, to summarize briefly these recent developments, central, prefectural, and local public health official organizations have been put in a supervisory position, while the main emphasis of the programs is now placed on the practical consultation of techniques—consultation which is being carried out largely through midwives and community-established maternal and child health centers.

It is no longer particularly necessary in Japan to create motivation for family planning or to provide general information about the subject. What is needed is to provide the people with more readily available opportunities for personal, intimate consultation about the techniques of contraception. It is generally recognized that it is through this kind of process that further reduction in induced abortions could be achieved.

Legalization of Induced Abortion

In 1948 a group of medical Diet members moved to submit a bill before the Diet for a national law which is now called the Eugenic Protection Law. Both the upper and lower houses soon passed the bill, and since then restrictions on the legal performance of induced abortion have been liberalized to a great extent as compared with the previous National Eugenic Law, which contained stringent conditions on its performance. It was stipulated that a legal induced abortion must be performed in conformity with the regulations prescribed in the Law and by a "designated physician" who had been authorized by the local medical association. Also, the Law has required the reporting of induced abortions by designated physicians. The numbers of induced abortions thus reported increased sharply until 1955, when 1.17 million abortions were recorded by health authorities. Since that time, however, the reported cases have decreased gradually.

Even today there are some speculations as to exactly why this Law was established. According to the original document produced by the promoters of the Law, however, the primary purpose was to bring into the open the already widely prevalent illegal induced abortions so that the undesirable effects associated with the clandestine performance of such operations could be eliminated. The document does mention the possible effect of such legalization on population control, but only as a secondary purpose. The real, primary emphasis was apparently on the protection of health.

Not a few experts tend to interpret this rapid growth in the number of induced abortions in postwar Japan as a continuation or a revival of old traditions which existed in the country some 100 or 200 years ago. During the years of Tokugawa Shogunate induced abortion and even infanticide were practiced by peasants at times of economic difficulty. It is clear, than, that the postwar induced abortion episode did not represent entirely a new experience to the Japanese people.

Induced abortion was a major factor in the decline in birth rate in Japan for at least ten years after the war. In the past several years, however, contraception has gained more impetus, and it is encouraging to note the downward trend in induced abortion since 1955, as mentioned above, though the rapidity of its decline was by no means great. Under the present circumstances, where the shortage of labor is often critical, and where the low level of Japan's birth rate is causing serious anxiety in some quarters of society, a number of voluntary movements are actively engaged in the efforts to further reduce induced abortions. Current opposition to induced abortion is mostly concerned with its moral aspects rather than its possible health hazards. Also, some persons have pointed out the inefficiency of induced abortion as a birth limitation means.

Pilot Projects of Family Planning

To conduct some pilot projects for the promotion of family planning for a demonstration purpose was favored particularly at the initial stage of the programs in Japan. Doctor Yoshio Koya initiated the development of this kind of program as early as in 1950, first in three typical rural villages and then among public relief populations and coal-mine workers. In all of these cases, the main significance was apparently attached to the possible implications of the projects, especially in terms of the government administration of family planning. As was anticipated, the projects gave a considerable stimulus not only to family planning workers but also to national leaders and political authorities. Levels of actual acceptance of contraceptive practice by the people, methods preferred, types of organizations required, trends in induced abortion after guidance—these were some of the topics which greatly interested the concerned observers.

An obvious criticism against pilot projects is that they operate under ideal conditions and that nothing practical can be learned from them because it is difficult to repeat the experiment under more difficult circumstances. Admittedly this criticism merits serious consideration, but at the same time one has to remember the strategic usefulness of giving a concrete and visible example to other groups who might be half-hearted where anything of pioneering nature is concerned.

Family Planning and Industrial Establishments

As described before, the government-sponsored programs for the promotion of family planning in Japan have been directed mainly toward the education of the general public through health centers and local communities. Apart from these government activities, another approach to family planning promotion that has proved highly successful involves the programs conducted by industrial establishments.

This type of project was initiated first about ten years ago by a few companies. Since then many major industrial establishments have followed the example and shown a great interest. According to the recent report, the total number of factories and companies rendering some service in this field is 55; they teach of family planning to some 1,240,000 individuals. In most cases, the establishment hires a certain number of well-trained midwives and public health nurses specifically for this purpose. Their wages are on the average quite good, and opportunities are frequently provided for them to attend refresher training courses. These instructors of family planning spend their time freely in the teaching of family planning practice through home visits.

Many reports of successful operation have come out of these programs; and there are a number of obvious advantages. When an establishment has its own housing project for employees, an instructor finds it much easier to make home visits among the clients who live close together than if she has to travel long distances in rural villages where people live apart from each other. Also, a similar level of education, income, and living among employees of the same company or factory makes it easier for her to provide group education. In most instances, the programs are conducted by agreement between employers and employees, and this facilitates the work of the instructor greatly, since well-planned organizations and a high degree of co-operation can be secured through mutual understanding. There are no significant problems with regard to financing of the programs; the establishment itself provides the necessary funds; contraceptive materials are supplied free of charge or at a nominal cost. Among other things, the total involvement of the whole community in the programs creates an ideal atmosphere under which contraception, family health, or even sex may be talked about freely with the instructor when she comes on her frequent home visits.

Stimulated by the success of these programs in the past few years, organizations which have huge numbers of employees, such as the National Railways, Police Departments, National Telegraph and Telephone Agencies have come to join in the programs. Their participation will no doubt have a substantial influence on the over-all situation of family planning promotion programs in Japan.

Government and Voluntary Organizations

In the experiences of family planning promotion of the Western countries, those responsible for actual education have, in most cases, been voluntary organizations. In developing countries today where it is necessary that the practice of family planning spread widely within a short span of time, it is generally recognized that the government has a major role to play. Certain advantages and disadvantages are found with regard to programs conducted by the government as well as by voluntary organizations.

In Asia, in general, the authority of a government is a real advantage when something must be done quickly on a nationwide basis. Once a policy is decided at the central level, it soon reaches the local level where actual programs are conducted; people regard the programs as important and pay full attention to them. Also, the government can provide a certain amount of money if it is convinced of real necessity, but voluntary organizations often find it difficult to maintain their activities financially in economically less advanced countries. On the other hand, the government action may have some drawbacks, such as an inability to move quickly, the inherent attitude of conservatism, or a too close involvement with politics. Voluntary organizations could take a liberal stand and adopt new and progressive steps as they think important.

However, it does appear that in developing countries the role of the government is of utmost importance. In many instances, the government is the only organization that has the means to reach the masses. According to a recent report about Mainland China, where birth control campaigns are extensively conducted by a government network, it is likely that their programs will proceed quite effectively and rapidly because of government sponsorship. Thus, in the promotion of family planning in Asian countries, the full participation, or at least the sympathetic co-operation of the government, seems most essential.

Family Planning as Population Control Policy

The importance of family planning as a means to control population growth is self-evident, and efforts to promote it must be increased. However, in the area of policy making, there is one point which requires careful consideration. If we talk about family planning entirely from the standpoint of population and try, as population control policy, to promote its practice through government channels only, we may encounter under some circumstances serious political and ideological antagonisms. Obviously, birth control is not a panacea to overpopulation, the solution of which requires many other considerations. A government advocating only family planning as a population control measure may be subjected to criticisms by national and local leaders to the effect that the government is so incompetent that it can do nothing but control births in coping with the present difficulties, which is seen as a negative position for a government to take.

Moreover, in the government-sponsored family planning programs, probably the best organization we can use is that of public health. It is important not only in family planning but also in all other aspects of public health to educate people in order to secure their full understanding about new programs. And, in the case of family planning, it is quite natural that ordinary men and women do not show much interest in the population of their country; they are interested in "population problems in their own homes."

For these reasons, it is very necessary for us to use proper explanations and proper means of approach, depending upon the circumstances and the audience. Japanese experiences in the last fifteen years have indicated that the best approach to the general masses is through maternal, child health, and welfare organizations.

Social and Cultural Changes

Practice of conception control cannot immediately be promoted simply by conducting some programs designed for that purpose, no matter how strenuous the efforts may be. Any visible change in the birth rate must come through concurrent changes in social, cultural and psychological factors among the people. The availability of the necessary materials of contraception and technical improvements of methods, important as they are, constitutes a secondary requisite in this sense. Much has been said about this point already by many experts, and I do not want to repeat the same discussion further, except to point out that Japanese experiences also are a good example along this line.

Family Planning as a Community Project

In the foregoing, the advisability of promoting family planning through public health organizations as part of maternal and child health services has been stressed. It follows from this discussion that family planning programs can best be conducted as part of community development programs. If we do not separate family planning from other community programs but rather integrate it with them, we would have certain practical advantages, such as, for example, the total involvement of the community, ready acceptance of the teaching, and, as mentioned above, the co-operation of local leaders. This consideration of conducting family planning programs at the community level is particularly important in those cases where we have to teach people on very basic levels, including motivational approach, and where solely supplying technical information about contraception is not sufficient.

7

The National Family
Planning Program
in Korea

JAE MO YANG

The Problem

Korea is one of the five nations of Asia that has established national policies and programs in support of family planning movements.

In Korea this national effort is aimed at lowering the birth rate among a predominantly rural population of approximately 27 million, with a density of some 270 persons per square kilometer. Korea's birth rate, according to a recent analysis of 1960 census figures, exceeds 40 per 1,000 population; our death rate is estimated at 11 per 1,000. The current rate of annual population increase of about 3 per cent places Korea among the most rapidly growing countries in the world. If this rate of growth continues, it is predicted that the population will double within twenty-three years and create a density of 380 persons per square kilometer by 1975.

The problem of excessive growth is intensified by the fact that, while only 21 per cent of the land in South Korea is arable, over 70 per cent of the people are engaged in farming, which is our major industry. This means that more than 1,300 persons must live on the harvest produced on 1 square kilometer of land. The average size of a farm in Korea is about 2 acres. However, more than 42 per cent of the farmers must try to make a living on less than 1.2 acres. The harvest from such small plots of land is inadequate even to feed the farmer's family, which on the average is six persons. This has resulted in an over-all national annual food deficit of 4.5 million *Suks,* or 810,000 tons of grain.

Korea, with an annual per capita income of between $70 and $80, is the poorest country in the temperate zone of the globe and perhaps among the most crowded in terms of housing. In urban areas the majority of families, which contain five members, live in one or two rooms, and in rural areas the average family of six must also crowd into a one- or two-room dwelling. It is estimated that 2 million houses are required to shelter adequately the present population.

The problem of excessive growth is likewise reflected in a shortage of educational facilities for children. For example, in 1960 there were 4,358,000 children in Korea between the ages of six and eleven, for whom elementary education is compulsory. This has resulted in classes containing 80 to 100 children in schools which even then must operate on morning and afternoon shifts.

Perhaps of even greater concern is the increasing number of children found abandoned on the streets, the reason for which is usually said to be poverty rather than illegitimate birth. At present, in the city of Seoul alone, six or seven abandoned children are picked up daily.

In relation to the achievement of Korea's Five Year Economic Development Plan, established in 1961, it is obvious that the goal of a 5 per cent annual growth rate cannot be reached unless a sharp reduction in the birth rate is effected. For example, in 1962 the economic growth rate was 2.6 per cent, as compared to an estimated 3 per cent population increase.

In recognition of the fact that gains made in improving our standard of living were being offset by concurrent gains in population growth, the national government included family planning in its Five Year Plan and set as goals the reduction of the rate of population growth to 2.5 per cent by 1966 and to 2.0 per cent by 1971.

Whether or not these goals can be reached, starting from scratch, is a matter of conjecture. However, it is certain that the government has launched a vigorous campaign to reduce population growth, which is being supported by all agencies and groups in Korea and by many international agencies outside of Korea.

Initiation, Early Progress, and Integration with Health Services

The first step initiated by the government in December, 1961, was to make the Ministry of Health and Social Affairs responsible for planning and carrying out a nationwide family planning program. The Ministry then proposed that the following steps be taken and policies established, which were in turn accepted and acted upon by the government.

1. To abolish all regulations restricting the importation of contraceptives as of December 6, 1961.

2. To encourage the domestic production and supply of contraceptives.

3. To establish a family planning advisory committee to advise the Minister of Health and Social Affairs.

4. To provide the necessary funds in order to establish a family planning clinic at all health centers.

Based on these actions and policies, in 1962, the development of the program was as follows:

1. A budget of approximately $336,000 was appropriated for the organization and operation of family planning services, the purchase of contraceptives, public information programs, and for vasectomy subsidies.

2. A family planning advisory committee was established within the Ministry of Health and Social Affairs.

3. Family planning clinics were established in each of the nation's 183 health centers.

4. 366 family planning workers were trained and 2 were assigned to each of the nation's 183 health centers.

5. A nationwide information program, including the production and distribution of printed materials and visual aids, was carried out.

6. Vasectomy operations were performed on 3,400 persons.

In 1962, 229,621 couples were registered in the Family Planning Program and given a choice of four contraceptive methods: foam tablet, jelly, condom, and diaphragm.

This brief summary of developments and progress in 1962 points out that the national program in Korea is firmly established as a responsibility of the Ministry of Health and Social Affairs—assuring its integration as a part of the nation's health services—and is being carried out through its network of health centers and referral to official and private hospitals. Also, I must mention that the Planned Parenthood Federation of Korea was established in April, 1961, and has provided assistance continuously in the development of the national program, particularly in the areas of training, public information, and research projects aimed at providing guidelines for the most effective implementation of the national effort. The nature of these research projects and their contributions to the national program will be discussed later.

Progress in 1963

The next step in continuing the development of the national program was the expansion and improvement of services. This step was fortunately made following the visit of a Population Council team of consultants headed by Dr. M. C. Balfour. Their evaluation of the program and suggestions for improvement were most helpful and were followed as closely as possible. For example, it was recommended that a national family planning advisory committee to the Minister be established, and that administrative and supervisory elements of the program be strengthened.

In February of 1962, an Advisory Committee consisting of representatives from official and voluntary agencies, business groups, and influential citizens was established and has met regularly ever since to review the program and make recommendations to the Minister.

In December, 1963, a family planning unit in the Maternal and Child Health Section of the Ministry was established and the staff was expanded to nine persons—two physicians and seven administrators. Also, a family planning supervisor was appointed for each of the nine provinces and two special cities.

Program development and progress in 1963 is briefly summarized as follows:

1. Appropriation of $593,077 as budgetary support.

2. 650 nurse-midwives received family planning training.

3. 330 surgeons received refresher training in vasectomy.

4. 23 obstetrician-gynecologist physicians were trained in the insertion of intra-uterine devices.

5. Vasectomy operations were performed on 23,000 persons.

6. Couples registered in the Family Planning Program were increased to 1,005,511.

A distinct highlight of the program in 1963 was the carrying out of a nationwide family planning enlightenment campaign, which not only succeeded in its objective of increasing attendance at family planning clinics, but, equally important, illustrated the willingness of other agencies and groups to participate in family planning activities. Particularly helpful were the Office of Public Information, in disseminating information through national mass media communication channels, and the 29,000 National Reconstruction Movement village workers, in contacting people residing in isolated areas.

Also, in 1963, instructions issued by the Prime Minister to the Economic Planning Board and seven ministries clearly outlined specific responsibilities and activities that they must assume and carry out in support of the effort to lower the rate of population growth. For example, the Economic Planning Board was ordered to establish a "Population Policy Council" to advise and make recommendations in the combined fields of population policies, family planning, employment, immigration, labor force exportation, and statistics. The Ministry of Education was to make a plan for the development of family planning curriculums and utilization of students for enlightenment campaigns. The Ministry of Justice was to study whether or not a eugenic protection law was advisable. The Ministry of Defence was to establish a plan to utilize the doctors in the armed forces to educate the soldiers. The Ministry of Cabinet Administration was to adopt the subject of family planning in their training programs for government officials.

Among the instructions to the Ministry of Health was the order also to establish a Family Planning Month, at which time intensive effort should be made urging the people to practice family planning. May was selected as the most appropriate month, as both Mothers' Day and Children's Day are observed during this month. Activities too numerous to mention were carried out in observance of the first Family Planning Month.

Therefore, by the end of 1963, a firm foundation had been laid for the growth and development of the national family planning program in Korea, and equally important steps had been taken to assure its continued support by all key official agencies.

In respect to the Planned Parenthood Federation of Korea and interested international groups, assurance of continued support in the development of the national program in 1964 was shown by increased financial and technical assistance and by firm commitments to carry out expanded co-operative activities in the areas of research, information, education, and training.

Current Developmental Progress

As a result of all these favorable factors, a national budget totaling $1,216,880 was appropriated for 1964 to carry out an expanded program, with major emphasis on the development of staff and the improvement of their ability to render services, including public information and education. Most important, the program is designed to enlist the support and participation of many more private physicians. This is an element on which, it is felt, the ultimate success of the family planning movement will depend.

In mid-1964 progress in carrying out the program, particularly in the development of staff and securing the participation of private physicians in the program, was progressing according to schedule.

For example:

1. 240 nurse-midwives were trained and 1 assigned to each of the nation's health centers. This raises the total number of family planning workers in health centers to 586.

2. 1,473 nonprofessional full-time family planning workers were given a brief training course and assigned to each township and to cities with populations ranging from 10,000 to 15,000. Their responsibility is primarily in the area of public information, education, and community organization, particularly in the establishment of mothers' clubs. They work under the supervision of the county health centers' family planning workers. Of these new workers, 500 will, by 1965, have received thirty days of additional training.

3. 30 ROK army surgeons were given refresher courses in vasectomy. The national goal for vasectomies this year is 40,000.

4. 115 obstetrician-gynecologist private physicians were trained in the insertion of intra-uterine devices, in anticipation that favorable results on current research into the use of these devices will be reported in the near future. It is hoped that 70,000 of these devices will be inserted.

Estimates as to the total number of couples who will be served on a monthly basis starting in July range from 280,000 to 300,000. This is more than double the number served during any single month of 1963. However, there are currently more than four times as many family planning field workers as there were in 1963.

The only serious threat to achievement of this estimated goal is the problem of supplies. Foreign exchange in Korea is limited, and even though it has, so far, been made available according to plan for the outside procurement of contraceptives, particularly condoms, the recent increase in the exchange rate will reduce by almost 50 per cent the remaining amount available for the purchase of dollars. However, by the end of this month, if all goes well, condoms will be produced in Korea. Modern equipment has been purchased by an industrial company, and anticipated production is 5,000 gross in May. But here again foreign exchange, although considerably less, will be required for latex and chemicals in order for production to continue.

In brief summary, the National Family Planning Program in Korea is a responsibility of the Ministry of Health and Social Affairs, specifically of the Maternal and Child Health Section, and is being carried out through the nation's network of health centers. Also, as we have seen, the program is receiving adequate budgetary support and the active co-operation of all official agencies concerned, by direction of the Prime Minister, and of many others both official and voluntary.

Development of the program to its present level has been rapid. Too rapid, perhaps, had it not been for the guidance and financial support it has received from outside sources, particularly the Population Council. Owing to this stabilizing influence, reinforced by consultative visits, the provision of a resident adviser, fellowship training, and, most important, the guidelines resulting from research projects, development of the national program has been kept in balance and as effective as possible.

For example, profiting from the experience gained in the study in Koyang Gun (or Koyang County) of the acceptability and effectiveness of traditional contraceptive methods among rural Korean families, both time and money have been saved in conducting surveys and in determining basic factors on which to develop the national program. From this study we were reasonably certain that 68 per cent of the eligible couples in Korea are interested in family planning, and that at least 30 per cent of them can be motivated to practice family planning. Acceptance, as we reasonably expected, was found to be highest among the twenty-five to thirty-nine age group, and specifically in this group among those who have two sons or three children. Also, as a guideline in the procurement of supplies, we are reasonably certain that, when condoms are available in adequate quantities, over 60 per cent of the participating couples will select condoms as the preferred form of contraception among the traditional methods.

Likewise, from the other research projects currently in progress in Korea and sponsored by the Population Council (such as the studies on intra-uterine devices, vasectomy, induced abortion, and the urban project), information and guidelines will be found to carry forward rapid but effective development of the national program.

Conclusion: Problems in Program Development

In concluding this brief outline of the development and progress to date of the Korean program, I would like to emphasize that, quite obviously, it is still in the beginning stage. In fact, it is so young that 1964 should be called its starting date in terms of the capacity to make an impact on our problem of excessive population growth. And even at this stage our expanded field staff, fresh from basic training, will require time in which to develop their capabilities. There are many other factors also, physical, social, and economic, which will impede their rate of progress, particularly in the rural areas. Lack of transportation will be a handicap limiting their range of contacts, as will a similar lack of communication facilities in carrying out mass media programs. Overcoming or modifying traditional attitudes and practices will take time; the practice of having many children—for reasons of security, status, ancestor worship, or income—is deeply ingrained, especially among rural people.

The lack of income with which to purchase contraceptives, coupled with the distance that must be walked to procure them, will, no doubt, be a heavy burden on the national budget and will, contribute to the irregular practice of contraception. The fact that little privacy exists in one-room homes tends, of course, to keep overt sexual preparations to a minimum; hence the many accidental pregnancies that have been reported.

It is hoped that help in attacking many of these physical and economic problems, will soon be available, following evaluation of the current intra-uterine study. So far, over 5,000 of these devices have been inserted at the twenty-four research clinics, and results of the study are in process of tabulation. If favorable, as anticipated, 139 obstetrician-gynecologist physicians who have been trained are to offer this service on a nationwide scale. More doctors are also scheduled for training. Also, help will be available in 1965 in the schools and universities to attack the problem of traditional attitudes and practices, since the subject of family planning has been included in study courses for 1965.

Finally, one other problem must be mentioned because of its importance both in development of the program and in securing continued adequate funds to support its effective operation. This is, of course, the need to develop improved methods of evaluation. Within the program itself a system of record-keeping and prompt reporting must be developed. This system must be simple and still provide all the basic data required to indicate both progress and the areas requiring immediate attention. At the national level, the collection, tabulation, and distribution of vital statistics must somehow be improved in order to reflect changes in births and deaths as quickly as possible. Korea is working closely with the Economic Planning Board and the Bureau of Statistics on this problem.

In conclusion, it is my firm belief that the national family planning program in Korea is established on a firm foundation and is in process of rapid but sound development as a result of the support it is receiving in Korea and from agencies abroad, such as the Population Council, the International Planned Parenthood Federation, the Asia Foundation, the Pathfinder Fund, and the Brush Foundation. We are indeed grateful for this help.

8

Family Planning Programs in Taiwan

BERNARD BERELSON

In the past few years Taiwan has become well known to those engaged in population work. The recent developments in family planning there have been important not only for that island itself but for the entire community of nations interested in lowering birth rates as a matter of public policy for the public welfare. While it is probably true that each country has its own conditions affecting the implementation of family planning, it is at least equally true that there is a certain commonalty among them, so that what works in one setting may work in another. In any case, the experience in Taiwan is worth reviewing not only for the substantive results that have been achieved there but also for the manner in which the program has been progressively reshaped to take into account new problems and new opportunities.

I wish to mention my Chinese friends who were unable to attend the Conference and who deserve the credit for what has been accomplished in Taiwan: Dr. S. C. Hsu of the Joint Commission on Rural Reconstruction, who has been the dynamic leader of population matters on the island; Dr. T. C. Hsu, Commissioner of the Provincial Health Department, who has had administrative responsibility for the program; Dr. C. L. Chen, Director of the Maternal and Child Health Institute (MCHI), who had jurisdiction over the Taichung program and the Pre-Pregnancy Health Program (PPHP); Dr. J. Y. Peng, who as Deputy Director of the MCHI ran the PPH and Taichung programs on a day-to-day basis; and Dr. L. P. Chow, who was trained at Johns Hopkins and who is now the senior specialist in charge of co-ordinating current activities in population. In addition, on the research side, I am indebted to John Takeshita and Ronald Freedman of the University of Michigan.

The developing program in Taiwan, to this point, can be clearly seen in three phases: the initial prepregnancy health effort, the Taichung experiment, and the current expansion.

The PPH Program

In April, 1960, the first prepregnancy health (PPH) program was begun in eight townships in Nantou *hsien,* near the Taichung center of maternal and child health activities in Taiwan. This was an experimental beginning to see whether nurse-midwives trained for family planning and working out of the health stations could be effective. This early experience was sufficiently favorable to warrant extension, and from November, 1961, to July, 1962, the program was expanded to 109 other health stations throughout the island, or 117 out of a total of about 360. This means that for the past few years about one-third of the health stations have had a full-time family planning worker on the staff. About half the workers were graduate nurse-midwives; they were given a week or so of training before assignment and a small kit of informational and educational materials for use in the field, at small meetings or in individual contacts. They offered, at cost, the condom and the foam tablet as the major methods of contraception, and each worker was given a monthly quota of contacting for the first time at least forty-five married women in the reproductive ages and of securing at least fifteen acceptors of family planning.

The program, understandably for a pioneering effort, was not without its problems. Since the workers were spread throughout the island, supervision was difficult; since they represented another pair of hands at the health stations, they were often assigned to other tasks by superior personnel; since they were relatively isolated, their morale frequently became a problem affecting their work; since they were required to meet a quota, they sometimes did so by encouraging persons already practicing contraception to use their own cheaper supplies, which, of course, did not affect the birth rate.

Despite such problems, however, the program does seem to have had some effect, at least where it was most closely supervised and most skillfully carried out, in the initial effort in Nantou. The Taiwan Population Studies Center, through Drs. Takeshita and Freedman, has done a careful analysis of data from the birth register for 918 matched cases—918 PPH cases "who accepted family planning guidance between April 1960 and September 1961" and their matched cases, i.e., matched in age, in education, in number of years married, in number of living children and sons at time of entry into the program, and, through proximity in the register, roughly in neighborhood. As their report concludes, "the comparisons show that reduction in the birth rate continues to be greater for the PPH cases than for the 'matches' suggesting that the PPH program has had some effect in achieving its purpose."

Birth Rate per 100 Woman-Years	PPH cases (918)		Matches (918)	
Birth rate in five years pre- ceding entry into program	37.6		33.2	
Birth rate from entry into pro- gram to Dec. 31, 1963	10.3		13.0	
Percentage reduction		72.6%		60.8%

The expanded PPH program through the health stations was about a year old when, in the form of the Taichung effort, the second phase was started. This program has received so much attention that it needs little detailed review here. Let me only mention its broad outline, the results to date, and some of the lessons we think we have learned.

The Taichung Program

This action program was carried on in Taichung City, an area, both rural and urban, with a population of about 300,000, or a target population of 36,000 married women aged twenty to thirty-nine, of whom 60 per cent had had three or more children. The 2,400 *lins* ("neighborhoods") in this city were distributed into a design with four "treatments"—nothing; mailings to high parity and newly married; personal contacts with wives only; personal contacts with both wives and husbands—cross-cutting three "densities." By density we mean the proportion of the *lins* in a geographical sector of the city that received personal visits from the field workers—in this case, a half in one sector, a third in another, and a fifth in the third. The program worked through the eight health stations in Taichung and the Maternal and Child Health Institute. It had eighteen nurse-midwives as field workers, plus nine supervisors, who used a kit of informational and educational materials prepared for meetings both for *lin* groups (an average of nearly four a week per supervisor) and with individuals (an average of forty home visits a week per field worker). Virtually all contraceptive methods were offered, including the diaphragm, the oral pill, and the new intra-uterine devices—the conventional methods at cost, the pills at 75 cents a cycle, and the IUD insertion for 75 cents. The evaluational efforts are threefold: (1) through the case records on home and clinic visits, (2) through a before-and-after survey of a random sample of 2,432 married women aged twenty to thirty-nine in Taichung City, and (3) through the fertility statistics of the official register. The action program began in mid-February, 1963, and ended in mid-October, but services and supplies have been available at the health stations since that date.

Below is a review of the major effects of the program:

1. On over-all acceptance: the basic data from case records (to May 1, 1964) are as follows:

	Within Taichung City	Outside Taichung City	Total
Intra-uterine devices	3,336	1,520	4,856
Traditional methods	1,156	25	1,181
Oral pills	142	9	151
Total	4,634	1,554	6,188

This table contains and implies a great deal. For example:

a. The acceptors within Taichung City are 13 per cent of all married women aged twenty to thirty-nine. Although, for technical reasons still under investigation (these figures may later be changed slightly), it now appears that the acceptors are 20–25 per cent of all those "eligible" (not already using contraceptives, pregnant, or sterile) and about 45 per cent of all those "currently eligible" (the previous group minus those wanting another child).

b. The intra-uterine device is the method of choice in nearly 80 per cent of the cases; the oral pill, mainly by reason of cost, is chosen by very few women.

c. The acceptors outside Taichung City, where no action program was carried on, are 25 per cent of the total—all through word-of-mouth influence of various kinds.

d. The traditional methods and the pill were distributed by home visit (85 per cent); the IUD came to be distributed mainly as the result of interest generated by word of mouth (75 per cent). Altogether only about 40 per cent of all acceptances resulted directly from home visits—an encouraging indication of the social momentum that can be generated by such a program.

2. As to trend: a program of this kind builds up quite rapidly, so that by the end of the second month, where in this case nearly 60 per cent of the initial home visits had been made, the acceptances hit a peak and held it for about a month before declining slowly to the rate of the last weeks of the action program itself. That rate, it should be noted, has been maintained steadily since the action effort was terminated last October—about 90 per cent of these later acceptors chose the IUD (as compared with 73 per cent during the program proper) and about 40 per cent of them lived outside Taichung City (as compared with 17 per cent during the program); both of these facts are evidence of the effectiveness of word of mouth in spreading the use of the IUD.

	Average Acceptances Per Week
February, 1963	114
March	101
April	134
May	159
June	115
July	108
August	113
September	71
October (end of active effort)	70
November	64
December	74
January, 1964	79
February	71
March	92
April	83
May	91

3. As to continuation: the six-month follow-up shows that 80 per cent of the IUD's were then still in place, as against continued use of traditional methods by only about 70 per cent of their acceptors. Thus

the IUD is not only more effective as a contraceptive in itself but also is more continuously used than the other methods (in this case, mainly condom and foam tablet). Indeed, about 12 per cent of those using traditional methods switched to IUD's during the six-month period. As a matter of fact, there is some indication that the spread of IUD's is accompanied by fewer complaints, fewer removals, and more reinsertions: it is obvious how these two tendencies reinforce one another from the following summary of the six-month follow-up on the use of IUD's.

Month of Insertion	Per Cent Continuing	Per Cent Removed	Per Cent Reinserted	Per Cent with Complaints
February	72	23	13	32
March	72	23	13	29
April	77	18	14	21
May	84	10	24	12
June	85	12	28	15
July	82	11	16	20
August	85	10	37	21

4. As to characteristics of acceptors: two key aspects of critical importance for such programs everywhere are that the unprogramed, "natural" spread of contraception has its first and largest effect among the better-educated and upper-income groups and that a programed, deliberate effort like this one has a small but important effect on the poorer, less-educated, rural masses, particularly on women of high parity. Mothers with four or more children made up more than two-thirds of the acceptors (as against 36 per cent of the "currently eligible"); women with no formal education, 30 per cent (as against 37 per cent); rural women, 35 per cent (as against 28 per cent); and, significantly for the future, women under thirty, 45 per cent (as against 58 per cent).

5. As to the design: "The proportion of those who accepted contraceptives was indeed higher in heavy density sectors, but this effect was almost completely within the 'everything' *lins* themselves. The indirect effect—the 'rub-off' from the home visits to the 'nothing' and 'mail' *lins*—was remarkably constant in the three sectors. The tentative conclusion is that the maximum return from minimum expenditure can be obtained with something less than the heavy sector degree of

concentration." (Bernard Berelson and Ronald Freedman, "A Study in Fertility Control," *Scientific American*, May, 1964, p. 36.) Moreover, the mailings did not seem to pay off—they did not promote the IUD's; contacting husbands, in addition to wives, did not pay off—the dominant method of contraception was a female one.

6. Finally, as to impact: here are three findings from the three modes of evaluation:

a. From case records: when the program began, about 18 per cent of the married women aged twenty to thirty-nine in Taichung City were practicing contraception; now about 27 per cent are practicing it (allowing for some acceptances by previous users who shifted to the IUD), or an increase of half again.

b. From the before-and-after survey: in late 1962, before the program began, 14.2 per cent of the women reported in the survey that they were then pregnant; in late 1963, 11.4 per cent of the *same* women reported pregnancy, for a decline of about one-fifth.

c. From the register: preliminarily, and still tentatively, the data from the register for January and February, 1964, show that the birth rate in Taichung City fell 17 per cent from the figure for the preceding January and February as compared to a decline of 10 per cent in all of Taiwan and a decline of 2 per cent to 10 per cent in the other major cities.

I would sum it all up in a single sentence: When interest in family planning is already widespread in a population of some literacy and considerable energy, and given an efficient means of contraception like the IUD and a supporting health network, then a deliberate effort can have a measurable impact on the birth rate within a year—and do so without creating any administrative, policy, or political problems for the program's leadership.

The Extended Program

Finally, the extended program is not unimportant, and a discussion of it serves to introduce the third and current phase of Taiwan's efforts in family planning. The government has not yet taken a firm position in favor of family planning, but governmental officers have considered that a "prepregnancy health" effort could be included in the regular health services. Encouraged both by the results in Taichung and by the absence of any opposition, these officers have moved into the third

phase which in a way combines the first two, with important exten-
sions.

The objective of the new program is to carry forward the family
planning and prepregnancy health work of the Provincial Health
Department in the context of local health improvement, primarily for
the more deprived segment of the Taiwanese population, both rural
and urban. To this end, the program will concentrate on the villages of
the salt, mining, and fishing regions and in the slum areas of the cities in
fifteen of the twenty-two administrative units of the province (counties
and cities). The particular districts in which the action effort is being
carried out have a population of 1.2 million, or about 10 per cent of the
total population of the island, and they are located in 100 townships
that have private obstetricians in practice, in order to provide for
insertion of IUD's. The 100 townships have a total population of 4.5
million; the 287 townships in the fifteen administrative units have about
85 per cent of the total population, or 10.3 million. Thus, again, there is
an opportunity for indirect effect outside the particular areas of the
action effort itself, since all the health station personnel can refer
interested cases to the private obstetrician-gynecologists.

Within the action areas, the program is carried out by teams of three
VHEN's (village health education nurse) given a month's training in
classroom and field. Each team spends a month in a village or a *li*
("section of a city") contacting about 350 families on the average; the
first half of the month is spent working on village health education (i.e.,
sanitation, nutrition, fly control, personal hygiene) and the second half
on family planning, again through meetings and personal contact.
There are now twenty such teams at work, and after July 1, 1964, there
will be thirty; the expectation is that the teams will cover 250 villages
(*lis*) in the first year, or about 500,000 persons, and 700,000 persons the
following year. The team administers questionnaires on fertility matters, a short version (10 minutes) to 80 per cent and a longer version
(30 minutes) to the other 20 per cent. They use posters and pamphlets
but no mass media.

This action effort also has an experimental design, though properly
not so elaborate as in Taichung. There are four treatments per township: (1) *lin* meetings in different frequencies, from every fourth *lin* to
every sixteenth, with one meeting concentrating on high parity cases
only; this effort is conducted by existing PPH personnel in areas where
the village health education program had already been carried out; (2)
VHEN's to every eighth village or *li* with home visits to every other *lin*,

or a ratio of 1 in 16 families; (3) VHEN's to every fourth village or *li* with home visits to every other *lin,* or a ratio of 1 in 8 families, and (4) VHEN's to every second village or *li,* with home visits to every other *lin,* or a ratio of 1 in 4 families. These four treatments are distributed more or less evenly to the 100 areas: 23, 31, 24, 22.

Under this system, and partly in consequence of the ambiguous governmental position toward family planning, the Provincial Health Department provides health education only through its personnel. Services and supplies are provided by an organization newly established for this purpose, the Maternal and Child Health Association (MCHA), officially chartered by the Ministry of the Interior and including over 200 medical and other interested people in its membership. The MCHA provides the traditional contraceptives for sale at cost and, in effect, contracts with private obstetrician-gynecologists and hospitals for insertion of the IUD's. Potential clients are given coupons to present to the doctors at the time of the insertion; the client pays $30NT (75 cents) and the coupon is redeemed by the MCHA for another $30NT, from a grant from counterpart funds. The payment to the doctors is meant to cover the usual follow-up as well as reinsertions where necessary. (Incidentally, the Medical Advisory Committee set up to monitor the Taichung experiment has cleared the IUD for this large expansion.)

This program got under way in March of 1964 and the period through June is considered to be a shakedown. Despite the normal trials and errors of such an experimental period, some impressive results can already be reported.

To begin with—and in my view this is a step of very great importance indeed—about 70 per cent of the 300 private obstetrician-gynecologists in Taiwan in the 100 experimental townships have now been trained in insertion of the IUD and are performing under the conditions just described. By the end of June, 1964, three-fourths of them will have been trained. Thus, this influential group, central to such an enterprise, now has the skills and the incentive to spread the use of the most effective and acceptable contraceptive method. What that has meant so far will be seen in a moment.

Although by the end of April the program had been operating in only half the indicated areas and for only a short time, the results had already begun to mount up. In March 1,191 IUD's were inserted and in April 2,253; the figures for May and June were 3,014 and 3,327. About one-third of the coupons distributed had already been redeemed.

(Only a few hundred acceptors of traditional methods were recruited, and the major emphasis is now being placed on the IUD.)

The sources of referral show the range of influence that has been established in the chosen areas (in approximate percentages):

PPH workers	35%
Obstetrician-gynecologists	35%
Health station workers	20%
VHEN's	10%
Private midwives	1%

The PPH worker, through previous efforts in her area, knows who the motivated women are; has a number of users of traditional methods who are glad to switch to this more convenient and more effective method (but only about 35 per cent of her referrals are "switchers"); has a larger population to deal with than the VHEN; and happens to be older, married, and better known in the area. The obstetrician-gynecologist now has a stake in the program. The health station worker refers women who come to the station for other services. The VHEN is stimulating and energizing, but her direct effects are far less than the indirect effects that go on around her; indeed, only about a third of the insertions from the visited areas are directly attributable to her. Thus, in short, the indirect effects are again, as in Taichung, much greater than the direct results of the home visiting system.

This is dramatically shown in another way: namely, the place of residence of the women accepting the IUD (see below).

Visited village	27%
Other village in township with program	36%
Other township	33%
Other county	1%
Unknown	3%

It can be seen that only about one-fourth the insertions take place in the areas receiving the intensive treatment.

The data on personal characteristics are by now familiar: 60 per cent in their thirties, but fully 27 per cent under thirty; 67 per cent with four or more children; fully 33 per cent with no formal education and 41 per cent with only primary schooling.

For various compelling reasons the family planning effort in Taiwan has been imbedded in an effort for local health improvement, and not all the reasons have to do with the needs of the family planning program itself. My own view is that if only the requirements of the family planning program were taken into account an even greater and faster impact could be made. But, as I said, the record so far is indeed impressive, and the Chinese officials on the island deserve the congratulations and gratitude of all of us for the ingenuity, energy, and skill they have brought to this task. The recent extension, incidentally, has raised no opposition or political objections: again, the people want the program, which is increasingly being recognized at the highest levels of government.*

In summary, then, a three-phase program of family planning has developed in Taiwan in only a few years—from the initial PPH effort through the Taichung experiment to the present program that combines features of both but in a new mix. The distance covered in the past two years has been great—in workers trained, in experience and knowledge gained, in program growth, in political support, and, as a basic criterion, in contraception effected in the areas covered.

* Indeed, since this talk was given, high-level officers of the government have spoken out in favor of the population program, and the effort described in the third section of this paper is now being extended to the largest cities in Taiwan.

9

Policies, Programs, and the Decline of Birth Rates: China and the Chinese Populations of East Asia*

IRENE B. TAEUBER

There are curious ironies in the associations among the population policies of governments, planned programs for the limitation of births, and reproductive behavior. Birth rates in the U.S.S.R. are comparable to those in the United States; rates in Japan are comparable to those in Western and Northern Europe. Neither the U.S.S.R. nor Japan has a population policy, but both countries have policies that permit induced abortions and encourage contraceptive practices. Induced abortions are the major means of limitation selected by the educated and motivated peoples of these recently developed countries.

The countries of Southern and Eastern Europe present similar conundrums. As late as 1950 their peoples, along with those of the U.S.S.R. and Japan, were placed by demographers in a transitional category, somewhere between the high birth rates of premodern agrarian societies and the low birth rates of the modern industrial

---

* This summary statement represents an analytical approach to the formulation of hypotheses concerning the population dynamics of the Chinese, whether in Mainland China or in the peripheral Pacific areas. The study of the demography of China is in progress; that of Japan was published as *The Population of Japan* by the Princeton University Press in 1958. The analysis of the demography of the people of the Pacific region is a continuing study of the Office of Population Research. Since the basic data are secured from the original statistical sources of the various governments that are, or have been, involved in governing the various areas, documentation is not possible in a paper as short as this one.

99

societies. Now all have moved to the low birth rate side of a simple dichotomy of the high and the low.

The European countries of recent decline have neither population policies nor action programs designed to reduce birth rates. In the Communist countries of Eastern Europe there are programs to protect the health of mothers and children and eliminate the deleterious effects of illegal induced abortions. Health activities provide the major means involved in the limitation of births. In Southern Europe, governments are traditionally Western and the people are Roman Catholic. Governments have neither health policies nor activities that sponsor or provide means of family limitation. Yet here also birth rates declined swiftly as highly motivated peoples found or developed means and facilities outside government.

These initial statements are the bases for six comments, three negative, three positive. First, government policies relevant to declining fertility and declining fertility itself are not related directly to the form of government or social organization. Communism structures the type of organization and the justification for service, but it does not preclude either effective action by government or insistent response by individuals. Second, religion is not necessarily a significant factor. The countries of rapid decline involve Roman and Eastern Catholicism, a Buddhist-Shinto-Confucian religious and ethical system, and official atheism. Third, culture, color, and continent do not have necessary relations to levels or dynamics of reproductive performance. The three negatives are portrayed in striking form in the simple fact that Japan, the U.S.S.R., and Italy are alike in having major recent declines in fertility.

The three positive statements are somewhat conjectural. Precipitant social change, disrupted traditions, and cultural shock are more conducive to family restriction than slow adjustments that preserve continuities. Furthermore, induced abortion has been a major factor in the rapid downward movements of birth rates. The sparsity of objective analysis of this role of induced abortion is an incomprehensible deficiency in the push of research into the hitherto neglected fields of human reproduction. Third, macroeconomic arguments place policy, programs, and response in the arena of controversy, whereas arguments related to the health of mothers and opportunities for children provide value contexts within which actions can be straightforward, services acceptable, and achievements appreciable.

Can we now extend the implications of these statements to Monsoon

Asia? Any answer is conjectural. Japan, the U.S.S.R., Eastern and Southern Europe—all have long records of economic, social, and educational advance. All are countries with ancient and proud cultures; there are traditions if not present facts of greatness. There were subjugations by alien powers, such as those of the Moors in Spain, the great Khan of the Mongols in Russia, and the Ottoman Turks in the Balkans, but these ancient conquests lacked the deeply corrosive impact of colonialism. Distinctiveness, however, is not an adequate base for an assumption of irrelevance, because lands, peoples, cultures, and times are always unique.

There is a beguiling temptation here. To assert the disassociations of policies, action programs, and reproductive behavior is to argue that schools of public health should return to traditional pursuits where techniques are known and achievements measurable. Curiosity and integrity alike dictate further exploration, as do the less scientific but none the less real forces of humanitarianism and a prevalent disbelief in the inconceivable. In much of Asia, peoples are vulnerable and famines are possible. Traditional birth rates along with controlled death rates generate the growth that bars economic development and sustains high birth rates. The treadmill cannot long continue.

A disinclination to articulate what may be or what could happen is found within Asia itself in the Chinese and the Chinese-related populations of the lands that reach in a vast arc from the waters of the Arctic to those of the Indian Ocean. Japan is in the forefront of demographic modernization—and so our previous generalizations concerning the countries of swift and recent declines in fertility cannot be irrelevant to China or the Chinese. Here also, far out in the Pacific, is Hawaii, where Chinese and Japanese who are two to three generations removed from indentured coolie status have lower birth rates, higher educational levels, and higher incomes than their Caucasian co-residents of the islands.

The people of the Ryukyu Islands have low birth rates. As a former prefecture of Japan under the residual sovereignty of Japan, this might be anticipated. As a responsibility of the armed forces of the United States, the open prevalence of induced abortion was definitely not to be anticipated. Moving southward in the peripheral area, there is Taiwan, where birth rates that were once the classic illustration of stability are declining in patterns quite reminiscent of those in Japan. There is no population policy, but there are prenatal services in health centers, induced abortions in the private sector, and an increasing acceptance of IUD's. The research staff of the experimental area in Taichung is prone to indicate that here birth rates are declining more rapidly than in Taipei, but all rates are declining. In Hong Kong, a birth rate that was initially rather low for a Chinese population is moving still lower. Further along the periphery, there is a declining birth rate among the Chinese in Singapore and Malaya.

These Chinese peoples of East Asia are responding to changing circumstances in much the same ways as the Japanese and the Europeans did. Rates of economic growth are high, and social mobility is substantial. People are restless and striving. In the sudden shift in direction of the society of the Celestial Kingdom ancient loyalties were shattered, new insecurities were born. Shock, disillusion, and disorganization contributed to rapid change, even in the reproductive mores that had persisted for millenniums.

Much can be debated about the present, and the future is not clear, but one thing is certain: Asia is no longer a monotone of high, stable birth rates. Birth rates are low or declining among all the Chinese or Chinese-related peoples along Asia's eastern periphery. Neither here nor elsewhere in Monsoon Asia are birth rates declining among peoples whose cultures are other than Chinese.

The great question is Mainland China. The population is large, the culture ancient, the setting until recently quite premodern except in a few port cities. The People's Republic inherited a largely illiterate peasant population with familial values of continuity, familial practices of selective infant care, a harsh struggle for survival, and high death rates. The premodern death rates could be reduced significantly through simple procedures, but the birth rate was another question.

Given the pragmatic habits of the Chinese, the limitation practices prevalent in the folkways, the potential for modernization seemingly inherent in the structure and dynamics of the society, and the achievement orientations of individuals, a China modernizing under almost any conditions would be expected to approach the lower ranges of the anticipated figures regarding population size.

Chinese communism has diffused cultural and social shock throughout the rural population. Ancient securities and verities are shattered; patterns of interpersonal relations are altered if not transformed. Family, sex, and age roles are shifted. The middle and older age groups may remember the old China with nostalgia, but those who are now in the early childbearing years have only childhood memories of a

China that was not communist. In five more years, those who are marrying and bearing their first children will have been born under communism.

The initial legal basis for family planning in Mainland China was Japanese, with contraception, induced abortion, and sterilization being available. The approach was cautious, with doctors of Western training or tradition repudiating induced abortion and arguing for diaphragms. In Mainland China, as elsewhere, conventional contraceptives presented in conventional ways wrought no revolution in the reproductive behavior of peasants. Since 1958 there has been movement to the communal form of organization, however modified, severe food deficiencies with widespread and distributed malnutrition, the extension of health facilities and paramedical personnel, and the strengthening of lines of communication down to local levels. New contraceptives became available and others could be anticipated.

If the question is asked as to whether Mainland China could reduce its birth rate if the decision were made to do so, the answer is affirmative. Administrative organization, personnel, and the other necessary means are available, and the people are conditioned to and disciplined by the regime. If the question is asked as to whether Communist China has made the decision to reduce birth rates, the answer seems also to be affirmative. Intra-uterine devices and induced abortion are both available. Motivations may still be somewhat below the levels essential for a great national increase in practice. Decisions are not quite voluntary, though, for nonconformity involves severe penalties. The bourgeois patterns of reckless childbearing remain possible, but in experimental areas an additional child beyond the third or fourth receives no rations.

To summarize, in Mainland China there is an ancient culture with rational mores. There is rapid social change, along with a planned shift in basic values. There is continuing communication and patterned indoctrination. There are feasible means of birth limitation in IUD's and induced abortion. There are health workers, and they, too, are or may be indoctrinated. The administrative lines of a police state permeate the population structure from metropolis to village. Psychic compulsions to conform and physical compulsions to eat alike strengthen the motivations to control fertility. A combined rationality of government and people in a concerted drive to reduce birth rates may be the pattern of the Chinese future. It is not yet certain that it will be so, for stability in course and superficial rationality in action have not been among the notable characteristics of the People's Republic. It is possible, though, that the first nondeveloped nation to achieve notable reductions in peasant, and therefore national, birth rates will be Communist China.

10

Discussion of Papers 6–9

MARSHALL C. BALFOUR

BALFOUR: It is my impression that the programs, at least those in the three countries whose activities have been described, have been successful or relatively successful. I shall now offer a few comments and raise questions about the individual reports.

Dr. Muramatsu has given us a clear and concise report on the events in Japan with respect to population and family planning. He reminded us that the 1961 decision of the cabinet in Japan was really, in a sense, a policy decision in support of family planning, even though this action was prompted primarily by the desire to reduce the number of abortions.

His second point dealt with the legalization of abortion, and I am glad he did not try to convince us that abortions are not legal in Japan. I recall a meeting in India some years ago, where a certain professor from Japan made a major point of explaining that abortions were not legal in Japan. The basis for his argument was, I believe, that not all of the 90,000 doctors in Japan were permitted to do abortions: only the prescribed physicians, some 12,000 or 14,000 obstetricians and gynecologists, could perform them. Dr. Muramatsu has cleared up this point. He has discussed clearly the role of pilot projects in Japan. Also, he described the important development in recent years of industrial and governmental agencies, such as the National Railways, which have active family planning programs. I would now like to question Dr. Muramatsu about some points not brought out in his paper.

Not too long ago an article appeared in *The New York Times* to the effect that the Japanese government and its officials were becoming quite concerned about their low birth rate. I wonder how this anxiety, if it persists, may affect government policy and birth control practice.

If Dr. Muramatsu dares to prophesy, I would also ask him what he thinks the future trend in the number of abortions will be. He noted that the maximum of 1.2 million abortions in 1955 has declined to about 900,000 annually. What is likely to happen in the future?

Although he mentioned some financial aspects of the program in Japan, economic details were limited. I would be interested to know who pays for the family planning activities and services in Japan. To what extent does the government meet the cost? To what extent do the private agencies contribute and to what extent do individual families bear the cost? It is my impression that the last group, the families, pay most of the actual cost of family planning.

Dr. Yang reviewed the developments in Korea during the past three years. Although he acknowledged some assistance from abroad, including that of the Population Council, I would emphasize that important actions were taken in Korea before the survey by an outside agency was made; a survey and recommendations were made in late 1962. At that date, governmental policy was already defined. Funds were appropriated for the first year and some personnel were trained and at work. I know also that the program in Korea is not merely a paper program, that is, something that is going to be done. Dr. Yang's report concerns what has been done and what is being done. I am convinced that more progress has been made in South Korea in population study and control than in any other Asian country in a comparable period of time.

In considering questions for Dr. Yang, I wonder sometimes about the hazards to the program. The risks of political instability and the factor of economic stress may create difficulties in the future.

I would like to ask Dr. Yang about the abortion situation in Korea. He did note in his paper that the Ministry of Justice had been asked by the Prime Minister to investigate whether a eugenic protection law was desirable or not.

Further, he reported that the Economic Planning Board of Korea requested the formation of a Population Policy Council. Has this been done? If it has been established, what are its functions and membership?

Dr. Berelson's report on Taiwan conveys the impression that much has been accomplished in both research and action in the face of difficulties. These difficulties, as implied in Dr. Berelson's report, come from the highest level of government; that is, the National Government of China has not yet adopted a firm policy with respect to population control. According to Dr. Berelson, the governmental position is still ambiguous.

Regarding economics, Dr. Berelson referred to the maximum return for the minimum expenditure but did not say anything about what this expenditure has been. I wonder if he has data or cares to elaborate on this point. In another paper about the Taiwan experience, the cost of family planning per acceptance was reported as something between $4 and $8 per family or per woman. That is a pretty wide range. Is it too early to ask how much family planning is costing or likely to cost in Taiwan?

Lastly, I found Dr. Taeuber's paper on China and Chinese populations most stimulating. As she suggested, it was something of a shock treatment. Dr. Taeuber has that capacity to shock us when it is timely. If I understood her paper correctly, she asserted that the birth rates of Chinese populations are declining. It will be interesting to observe the evidence in due course. Dr. Taeuber did state that birth rates are low or declining among all the Chinese or Chinese-related people along Asia's eastern periphery. And as she elaborated, she brought in Korea and Japan as "Chinese-related," so perhaps the statement becomes more plausible.

TAEUBER: Japan is now low.

BALFOUR: Regarding her hopeful and optimistic feeling about future birth rates in Mainland China and among Chinese populations, I do agree in general, because I have spoken and written with some optimism, supported by faith, that Asia's population problem will be solved or will be ameliorated before catastrophe results. However, to her final sentence I do take some exception.

She states, "It is possible . . . that the first nondeveloped nation to achieve notable reductions in peasant, and therefore national, birth rates will be Communist China." Possibly that will be so. However, I feel the need of more factual information as to what is really happening in Mainland China today. Certainly the information we get is scarce; there are bits of news here and there about changes that are taking place. Personally, I hesitate to accept Dr. Taeuber's view that Communist China will probably be the first undeveloped nation to achieve a notable reduction in population size. It would surprise me less to see Korea and Taiwan and perhaps even India show significant declines in birth rates before there is evidence of such reductions in Communist China.

CHAIRMAN HUME: Thank you, Dr. Balfour. I think we are now ready for a discussion. Dr. Muramatsu, would you like to reflect?

MURAMATSU: I was interested to know about the article that appeared in *The New York Times* with regard to Japan's anxiety about her low birth rate. It is true that such an anxiety exists among some of the government officials and political leaders.

In my opinion, there are a number of factors contributing to this attitude: the fact that Japan's birth rate now ranks fifth or so from the bottom in the world; the large numbers of youths now leaving farms for cities where they hope to find a more satisfying life (out of a total of forty-six prefectures in Japan, twenty-three more or less agrarian prefectures lost their populations to a different degree during the last intercensal period, thus making the farming industry dependent mostly on the labor of housewives and the aged); the shortage of skilled labor often complained of by proprietors of medium- and small-sized enterprises; a foreseeable aging of the population; and the inherent unpleasantness associated with the idea of "cutting down the numbers."

Apparently many of these recent social and economic changes are not the direct consequences of family planning promotion itself; they have been brought about primarily by the people's aspiration for better opportunities, better jobs, and better life. Nevertheless, some quarters of the society tend to think that all of these transitions are due to the encouragement of family planning. In their eyes, it appears that Japan has done too much family planning. Amendments to the Eugenic Protection Law to the effect that induced abortion should be more strictly controlled with regard to legal restrictions have been discussed by a group of women leaders in the Diet. Some economists and national planners also hope to see a large-scale curtailment in the number of induced abortions.

At the same time, however, an equal number of government officials is aware of the fact that it is the people who are demanding and practicing family planning and induced abortion. The official policy decision and the actual programs designed to promote family planning practice admittedly have exerted some influence, but the relative role played by these actions is apparently limited. Even without the government's support and participation, the present level of family limitation practice would have been reached anyway, though, perhaps, a longer period of time might have been required to do so. Thus, the majority of the people has a strong desire for small families. Furthermore, over-all attitudinal changes generated after the war among the Japanese tend to push them toward the direction of self-determination. Even if more births were encouraged by the powers that be, it is doubtful to what extent such an attempt would be successful.

As a result of these considerations, it is likely that the Japanese government will shift the emphasis in their programs from the quantitative aspect of population to the qualitative aspect. This would mean that appropriations of the government budget explicitly earmarked for family planning would diminish year after year, with the understanding that Japan has already reached a stage where family planning is a matter which should be entirely left to the decision and desire of each individual and that there is no longer a specific need for the government to take action in this field. On the other hand, the government has already taken interest in programs aimed at the betterment of the quality of population and the social development whereby the potentiality of human resources available can be fully developed and utilized.

In conclusion, my personal view on this matter is that we shall see fewer and fewer official efforts in family planning action programs but that family planning practice itself among the people will grow or at least maintain its present level, since the idea of controlled family size is so firmly ingrained in the minds of the people.

As regards the future course of induced abortion figures, nobody, of course, can offer a definite answer. My personal estimation is that the downward trend we have been observing for the past several years in abortions will continue but at a slower rate.

Finally, I am sure that Dr. Balfour is right in his impression that it is the families who pay most of the cost of family planning. In these years there has been a certain amount of the government's budget allocated to family planning, including subsidies to help indigent people in their procurement of the necessary contraceptive materials. But the total figures are not high. If you compare the Japanese figures with those of other Asian countries where governments are interested in birth control (with adjustments for the difference in population size, rate of currency exchange, and the actual modes by which the budget is finally consumed), you will find that the government contribution in Japan is relatively small.

CHAIRMAN HUME: Thank you, Dr. Muramatsu. Dr. Yang, I wonder if you would like to reply to the questions that Dr. Balfour directed to you?

YANG: Dr. Balfour mentioned the hazards and instability in the political situation in Korea. It is true that we have had many changes in the cabinet members. For example, a few weeks ago there was an overnight turnover at the highest political level and the cabinet was changed. As you know, family planning is a long-term project. So, without political and economic stabilization, we can hardly expect any planning or motivation, particularly among those people who are living day by day.

I think Dr. Balfour asked about our Population Policy Council and also the Economic Planning Board. These organizations have also been affected by the frequent changes in the government organization. I was asked only several months ago to be a member of this Population Policy Council, but a few days later the Economic Planning Board was changed to an internal organization and the man responsible for planning the Population Policy Council was also transferred to another job. So, since we have a new cabinet now, it will take a few months until we can establish a Population Policy Council.

As for the induced abortions in Korea, I have very little reliable statistical data. There are some data available from our rural family planning pilot study, which was conducted in an area about 15 miles north of the capital city.

There were about 1,400 couples in our study area and 1,700 couples in the control area. The study and control areas were pretty well segregated in terms of communication and transportation by an intervening river. In the study area we had 628 so-called contraceptors among the 1,400 couples. Among those 628 couples, we observed 119 accidental pregnancies during the period of eighteen months from October, 1962, to March, 1964. Out of these 119 accidental pregnancies, 51 were resolved by induced abortion, which we never encouraged. During the one year of 1963, there were 99 births and 20 induced abortions in this area.

Although induced abortion is illegal in Korea at the present time, we estimate, according to these statistics from small areas, that there is a considerably high abortion rate, particularly in urban areas such as Seoul City. By chronological observation this abortion rate is getting higher every year. We feel some responsibility for this trend in induced abortion because it illustrates that people are motivated to reduce pregnancies.

The condom users among these 628 contraceptors had a pregnancy rate of 17 and foam tablets gave a pregnancy rate of 38.5. This means, particularly in rural areas where the privacy is limited, that there are relatively high pregnancy rates.

Thus, we may say that we have motivated the people to accept the idea of family limitation in Korea. Most couples desire to have an average of 4.4 children. They want to have at least two boys. However, this desired number is usually obtained by the time the wife reaches thirty or thirty-five years of age, when she still has ten to fifteen more years before her childbearing years are over. If we continue such contraceptive methods in our service which have a fairly high failure rate, then people may lose interest in seeking help or advice from our service. For this reason, we are very eager to find simple methods which are also effective in terms of prevention of pregnancy, such as intra-uterine devices.

Concerning this high accidental pregnancy rate, I would like to mention a difficulty we have in securing enough governmental budget for importation of contraceptives, particularly condoms. In the past three or four months we have had good attendance in our health center clinics. However, the stock of condoms has run out and the Ministry of Health issued an order to all family planning clinics to encourage the patients to wash the condom and re-use it. In this study area, the condom users had 17 accidental pregnancies, even though we supplied them with enough condoms. If we encourage the re-use of the condom, I do not think people can practice it effectively because of the lack of privacy or other difficulties.

Regarding the legalization of induced abortion, we have divided opinions among the government leaders. One group, which consists of those working at the Economic Planning Board, believes that if it were legalized, it would have a great effect in reducing the birth rate. However, I rather doubt that such legalization will effect an increase in induced abortions, since induced abortion is highly dependent upon the standard of living, motivation, general economic standard, and so on. I do not think the total number of induced abortions would change much with the legalization. We are therefore not encouraging acceptance of this idea.

The other group, particularly a group of medical doctors, realizes the high risk arising from illegal abortions; since most of the qualified doctors and hospitals are not open for illegal abortions, those people wanting to have induced abortion seek nonqualified clinics or doctors. Under such conditions, the risk may be high. So, we must at least take some measures to prevent these hazards.

Recently, the Minister of Health organized a committee; the Planned Parenthood Federation, the Maternal and Child Health and the Pediatric Associations, and also the Obstetrics and Gynecology Association are all represented in this committee, which is to discuss a possible establishment of a maternal and child health law. The committee is chiefly concerned with the betterment of maternal and child health and the financial aspect. However, in the last chapter of the draft for this maternal and child health law are included the provisions concerning induced abortion.

A few months ago, a man who is interested in economics and population became a member of Parliament and publicized that he was preparing a eugenic protection law. He explained to newspapermen that this law would approve induced abortion for any woman who wanted it, if she had more than two children. This stimulated the Catholic groups in Korea, who took this chance to oppose with an organized effort not only the proposed induced abortion law but also the whole idea of family planning.

CHAIRMAN HUME: Thank you, Dr. Yang.

Now, I want to make sure that Dr. Berelson has an opportunity to speak. However, Dr. Berelson, it would be well if you replied now to Dr. Balfour's questions and then perhaps Dr. Taeuber would like to amplify her remarks.

BERELSON: As regards the cost, I cannot say very much more than what was said before. Of course, the average cost of acceptors is coming down. It is going to be given a full analysis next year. The real trick is to tie the cost to that experimental design of ours and see how much it cost per acceptor in the various areas, but that has not been done yet.

Dr. Balfour is quite right in calling our attention to the economic problems involved in the spread of family planning. If it did cost, say, $5 an acceptor in Taichung, it certainly was a valuable economic investment at that rate and at a lot more than that, I believe.

The economic motive is involved in various ways. One of the reasons I believe that the IUD was spread so rapidly in Taichung was that 80 per cent of the 75 cents for the insertion was split as supplementary income among the health station people. They had an economic incentive in spreading this program, which is why I emphasized that the private obstetrician-gynecologists have an economic incentive in Taiwan just as the authorized physicians in Japan have an economic motive and are actually organized to protect it.

The general cost of these family planning programs is something that we will have to look at. Dr. Sadik, Dr. Rao, and Dr. Moore can correct me. The last time I looked at the figures, the National Programs in India and Pakistan were about 1 cent per capita per year for family planning and in Korea it is about 4.5 cents per year, which would make a difference. The Turkish program is budgeted for about a nickel per capita per year. I have developed a rule of thumb that you have to have a nickel per capita per year in order to make a significant impact.

Finally, Dr. Balfour will be interested to know that we were told by one of the private doctors that when the Taichung program got under way, one of the indirect effects was to cut the cost of abortion in Taichung by half.

CHAIRMAN HUME: Dr. Peng, I wonder if you would like to add a few comments to Dr. Berelson's remarks.

PENG: We have shown a good example of basic use of financial assistance from the U.N. and other organizations. This is another good example of the best use of technical materials and people. We do not need to be motivated, but we need the acceptance of contraception.

About our health services, our private doctors are very well distributed. We just put additional effort into the program in order to give the services to our people. I think we have reached about the same situation that Japan had in 1957.

CHAIRMAN HUME: Thank you very much. I wonder if Dr. Taeuber would like to say something?

TAEUBER: I would rather throw it open for discussion.

CHAIRMAN HUME: Then we will throw this open for discussion.

BERELSON: Mr. Chairman, may I ask Dr. Taeuber some questions?

CHAIRMAN HUME: Yes, sir.

BERELSON: Dr. Taeuber, I found your presentation extremely interesting. When you were speaking about the spread of family planning in different cultures and so on, there were some different phrases and different geographical areas. I think it was Dudley Kirk who first brought it to my attention that, while family planning had indeed spread across different political ideologies and different religions, East and West, wealthy countries and poor countries, industrial nations and agricultural nations, it had not spread from the temperate zones to the tropical and semitropical zones. Is that a serious factor? What observations would you care to make?

Second question: did you mean to imply that the birth rate of Mainland China will come down in the absence of a deliberate plan, presumably governmental effort?

TAEUBER: I suggested that Mainland China was the first country to show an early decline in the peasant birth rate among nondeveloped countries. This was phrased rather carefully. I think it is safe to say that both Taiwan and Korea had long periods of economic development, education advance, and substantial modernization prior to the present period. One of the factors which make the great difference in what is happening to birth rates is that there has not been such rapid economic development in Mainland China as there has been in these other areas.

There are immense complexities here. Communist China has a system. It has developed a system which has smashed the basic barriers of culture, and in the absence of specific governmental policy, this should be conducive to decline.

Given the food difficulties, given the prevention of rather ghastly famine by the Canadian wheat, given the uncertainty in sources of food, there are certainly strong reasons for any rational people to attack directly the problem of rural growth. All I am really saying here is this: given the type of peasant population which has never had a high birth rate in rural terms, which is ridden with control and remained so until the Communists came in, given the absence of religion, given what communism itself has meant, given what we know from Taiwan, Korea, and elsewhere that induced abortion is compatible with the culture and that IUD's are acceptable—this is a setting in which the government could effect a decline in birth rates, if it so rules.

About the statistics, the collection of statistics is not a responsibility that has been assigned to us. We do not know. We do not know whether the Chinese themselves know.

About the first question, I am immensely disturbed by the rising tide of color and all this kind of argument. I am equally disturbed by the prevalent climatic differentiations of the world. When I complete the study of climate then I may have more data, but I would guess that this is basically a derivative of a geographical distribution of a wide variety of other factors. I cannot quite go for a revival of Ellsworth Huntington, which is what we are having in some intellectual circles.

CHAIRMAN HUME: Any other questions?

HILL: I would like to pose a question which may not necessarily be answered here in the time that we have left, but since we have another day, there may be some thoughts on the matter from the other speakers.

It seems to me that in the action program the assumption has been made that our target is the individual couple and primarily the woman.

We do know that the birth rate is made up of increases and decreases in births; and the birth rate is made up not just from births that occur after the third or fourth child but is a function of the timing of births, or the spacing of births. Is there any consideration of targets other than the couple? There is a timing of marriage in many countries that is not in the hands of the couple, necessarily. The timing of the first child is the interval between marriage and the first child. Who makes this particular decision? What pressures are brought to bear on it? Is it not merely a consequence of marriage? But the interval between marriage and the first birth is so variable across the world that it is suggested that there is orderliness in the phenomenon itself.

Now, I am wondering, in addition to the notion of an ideal family size which you identified as 4.4 for Korea, for example, what are the preferences on ages of marriage that are changing? Is the optimum age for bearing children before twenty? In the twenties? In the thirties? What are optimum spacing intervals? When you get down to these matters, then you are getting down into what involves decisions sometimes made by the couple and sometimes made with other people involved.

Is our action program so clearly focused on this one target because it happens to be the target that has been so clearly in focus in Western civilization?

CHAIRMAN HUME: Would anyone else like to comment?

TAEUBER: In the countries that have become interested in reducing their rates of growth, the first action is to pass a law raising the age of marriage, which is about as effective as passing a law that says there will be fifteen months between marriage and the birth of first child.

I think the concentration on the limitation of childbearing in this Conference is for two specific reasons. One, this is a conference held under the auspices of the School of Public Health; it considers in the main the areas in which public health personnel become involved. But, over and beyond that, there have been a wide variety of analyses made of laws on the age of marriage, and these are diversionary undertakings. It is not sufficient to secure that level of reduction in fertility which will contribute much to reducing the birth rate in a country.

HILL: Passing a law is only one way.

TAEUBER: But the fundamental thing is in terms of adequacy. In Taiwan, you can get the percentage married by single years of age. The percentage married at the younger ages has been going up at least since 1915. This has been advancing in Japan throughout the period of record. This is beautifully patterned in Japan and in other areas of record, and the correlation between birth rates at the younger ages and marriage rates at those same ages is almost one. The answer is that marriage is so deeply imbedded in the institution, in very many of these cultures, that a social and not necessarily permanent ceremony occurs. If there then is a pregnancy and particularly a production of a son, and if there is compatibility between the daughter-in-law and the mother-in-law, this then becomes a legal marriage, enters the marriage statistics, and becomes a permanent sex relationship. But in the traditional societies this is likely to become a highly intricate area. This is where the sociologist should come in.

MURAMATSU: What about Mainland China? Have you any information about the age of marriage?

TAEUBER: I will make my classic statement. There is not a single thing on the population of Mainland China which is now or ever has been known throughout the history of China.

SADIK: We have raised our marriage age from fourteen to sixteen and we want to raise it further to eighteen. But many births are not registered, and so nobody knows when a person was born. If a person says fourteen, sixteen, or eighteen, you have to accept it. We have a lot of social reform laws under consideration, such as raising the age of marriage and child labor laws, but enforcing these laws is difficult for the simple reason that we do not have birth certificates and must rely on what the mother or father says.

PART II

PROGRAMS IN
THE WESTERN HEMISPHERE

11

Voluntary Agencies

ALAN F. GUTTMACHER

Contraception preceded the white man to America. It is reported that at times the Indian brave and his squaw partook of a tea brewed from *lithospermum ruderale* in the attempt to control fertility. A letter from Jonathan Edwards leaves no doubt that the technique of coitus interruptus was known and condemned by the Puritan fathers. There is, however, little evidence that any method of birth control was widely practiced by Americans until centuries later.

In 1831, a seventy-two-page tract by Robert Dale Owen, "Moral Physiology," introduced contraception to the American public. It advocated the use of withdrawal; the booklet was so eagerly accepted that five editions were printed the first year. Owen's efforts inspired a Boston physician, Charles Knowlton, to publish "Fruits of Philosophy" a year later. In it he recommended the postcoital douche as a contraceptive. Knowlton, despite the medical distinction of being a Fellow of the Massachusetts Medical Society, was rewarded by three months at hard labor in the East Cambridge jail.

Such pioneer efforts were kept alive in succeeding decades by individual physicians and laymen. Perhaps the two most influential representatives of the medical profession were Abraham Jacobi and Robert L. Dickinson.

Dr. Jacobi had been jailed for his part in the 1848 Austrian revolution and had then emigrated to America. Among his very numerous accomplishments he founded the *American Journal of Obstetrics and Diseases of Children,* now the *American Journal of Obetetrics and Gynecology,* and made pediatrics a specialty in the United States.

Dr. Jacobi, in his presidential address before the American Medical Association in 1912, said: "It has become an indispensable suggestion that only a certain number of babies should be born into the world. As long as the well-to-do limit the number of their offspring, the advice to the poor to limit the number of their children is perhaps more than merely excusable." In discussing the large family among the poor and those who failed to grow to adulthood, he said of the children who had succumbed: "For the interests of the latter, and the health of the community at large, they had better not have been born." This was spoken in 1912 to the American Medical Association.

I think Dr. Dickinson's contributions probably need no telling in this group because many of us knew him personally, but perhaps his most important contribution in this area was a very excellent review which he wrote in 1924, "Contraception: A Medical Review of the Situation." It was published in the *American Journal of Obstetrics and Diseases of Children* and was the first authoritative article on the topic by an important American gynecologist. It was written as a deliberate challenge to the restrictive federal postal laws, since it was widely mailed in a medical journal and as a separate reprint. He proved that the medical eminence of an author is likely to grant immunity from some types of legal prosecution.

We must remember that in 1869, Anthony Comstock, through the Society for the Suppression of Vice, had caused contraception to be included in an obscenity law passed by the Legislature of the State of New York. Four years later he engineered the passage of an anti-contraceptive law through the United States Congress.

The legal barriers established were so strong that druggists, hospitals, and even doctors were afraid to use the mails for contraceptive advice or to do anything in this area that might make them vulnerable to criminal prosecution.

There was no organized birth control movement in the Western Hemisphere until Margaret Higgins Sanger, born in Corning, New York, during the eighteen-eighties, the sixth child of a family of eleven, gave it leadership. After training as a nurse, marrying, producing three children, and taking the cure for tuberculosis, this titian-haired thirty-year-old beautiful woman launched her epoch-making career in 1912 by publishing articles in *The Call*, the leading New York socialist paper, on "What Every Woman Should Know" and "What Every Girl Should Know." Her theme was the emancipation of woman from sexual servitude through contraception.

It is important to point out that in both the United States and England, and perhaps other areas, the birth control movement was initiated by a group of earnest feminists. They were not primarily interested in family planning or the child-spacing of Malthusianism. They were interested in equalizing the socioeconomic and political status of women with that of men. Contraceptive knowledge was simply one important weapon of their arsenal in the war for feminine liberation. In 1929 Margaret Sanger wrote that in 1914 she began "to advocate contraception on feministic and libertarian grounds."

The first American birth control organization, The Voluntary Parenthood League, was organized in 1914, just fifty years ago, by Mary Ware Dennett and others interested in the feminist movement. This was done during Margaret Sanger's enforced absence abroad. She had sailed the day she was to be tried for breaking the Post Office ban against the mailing of contraceptive literature.

During the European banishment, she coined the phrase "birth control" and established important friendships with Marie Stopes and Havelock Ellis in England and Drs. Rutgers and Jacobs, who, thirty-five years before, had opened the world's first contraceptive clinic in the Netherlands.

On October 16, 1916, Mrs. Sanger opened the first birth control clinic in the United States, in the Brownsville section of Brooklyn. In the forty-eight years since then, 249 clinics have been established in the United States.

Birth control leagues meanwhile had been started in several cities throughout the country, and in 1917 they were united under the name of the National Birth Control League, with Mrs. Sanger as president. The organization changed its name to the American Birth Control League in 1921, and in 1942 the current name of the organization, the Planned Parenthood Federation of America, Inc., was chosen.

Time does not suffice to develop the history of the North American birth control movement step by step. I wish to point out a few meaningful events.

In 1931 a resolution supporting birth control was endorsed by the Public Health Committee of the distinguished New York Academy of Medicine. Since then, many medical organizations have given their endorsement; among them: the American Medical Association in 1937, the American Public Health Association in 1959, and the American College of Obstetricians and Gynecologists in 1963.

In 1936 an important decision was rendered by the United States Court of Appeals for the Second Circuit establishing the legality of birth control under medical auspices. The three judges ruled in the now famous case of "U.S. versus one package" that the federal birth control statute was not intended "to prevent the importation, sale or carriage by mail of things which might intelligently be employed by conscientious physicians for the purpose of saving life or promoting the well-being of their patients."

In all states but Connecticut and Massachusetts, the federal legal emancipation was applied by court decree or custom to the individual state laws on birth control, thus permitting doctors and medically supervised agencies to prescribe contraceptives.

As you know, the now famous Connecticut case is going to be retried by Fowler Harper, the distinguished professor of law at Yale, who will plead the case before the Supreme Court. Mr. Harper, whom I saw in Miami one week ago, says that he is now preparing his brief. The case is likely to be argued in February, 1965, and a decision rendered by the U.S. Supreme Court before June of 1965. The Planned Parenthood Association is going to present an *amicus curiae* brief, and the actual case will be carried by the Planned Parenthood League of Connecticut in behalf of the two defendants, Dr. Lee Buxton, professor of obstetrics-gynecology at Yale Medical School, the physician titularly in charge of the New Haven Planned Parenthood Clinic, and Mrs. Griswold, its executive director.*

In 1942 the United States Public Health Service initiated the policy of according requests from state health officers for birth control programs the same consideration and support it gives other state public health programs. Since 1942 contraceptive services have been offered in the state health programs of Virginia, the Carolinas, Alabama, Georgia, Mississippi, and Florida.

The rendering of birth control service in these seven states is wholly at the option of the individual county health officer and is therefore spotty and sparse in distribution. Funding is from the state's Maternal and Child Health Federal allotment. I just returned from a survey of Florida and can report that forty-eight of the sixty-three counties in Florida give birth control, through the county health department, to the people who seek it. This sounds wonderful, but it is actually not very meaningful because in some counties only 3 patients got birth control help in 1963 and in others, like West Palm Beach County, only 790 were aided, so that the number varies tremendously. In some counties the rule is that birth control can only be given to a woman

---

* In the spring of 1965 the Supreme Court ruled unconstitutional the 1879 Connecticut law that made it illegal for anyone, married or otherwise, to use contraceptives.

who is living with her legal spouse who has produced six children; in other counties all that is required is that the woman has produced one child. So, it obviously is a very rough type of service from the point of view of equality of opportunity.

Dr. Sowder, Florida's state health commissioner, is very anxious to invigorate the program. He said to me, "We are just taking that part of the iceberg which sticks above the water." I think the part of the iceberg above water is about one-tenth; if that is the case and they gave 5,000 patients birth control in 1963, when we "take" the whole iceberg it will be 50,000 patients. Unfortunately, none of the seven southeastern public health birth control states does a meaningful job as yet.

Fortunately, other states are conducting birth control clinics through their county health departments and these are more impressive than the seven southern states. Among the leaders are California, Maryland, Kentucky, and Tennessee.

In 1952 the United States became one of eight founding nations of the International Planned Parenthood Federation, a Federation which now includes thirty-five member nations. The International Federation operates through five regional groups: Europe–Mid-East–Africa, obviously a very large region which they soon hope to split up into two and the Western Hemisphere region which includes Latin and North America. Eventually this will also be split into two regions (for a total of seven regions). The single regions are: Indian Ocean, Southeast Asia, Western Pacific. The regional headquarters of the seven member nations now forming the Western Hemisphere Region is located in New York City.

In 1960, under the serious threat of expanding world population, the World Population Emergency Campaign was launched by Mr. Hugh Moore and General William Draper. The purpose was to raise American funds for the International Planned Parenthood Federation. Since the main sources of financial support for this new organization duplicated those of the American Planned Parenthood Federation, the two were amalgamated a year later, to prevent confusion, under the present name: Planned Parenthood-World Population.

Let us analyze how Planned Parenthood-World Population operates today.

As noted earlier, it began as a feminist organization and after feminist goals were largely achieved, the female leadership which then guided its activities concentrated on family planning. Today the national leadership has passed largely into the hands of men. I am very much interested when I attend the Executive Committee meeting or the Board meeting of Planned Parenthood today that the majority present are men. The efforts of the organization are twofold: they are equally directed toward having birth control services made available through existing health agencies to all who cannot afford private doctors and toward contributing the maximum effort to helping the world achieve a slower rate of population growth.

On January 1, 1964, there were Planned Parenthood affiliates in 106 United States cities. It is likely that several additional cities will be added during 1964, since there are 78 new communities seeking affiliation.

There are three types of affiliates. The standard, and by far the most common, is the affiliate which operates one or more centers to provide clinical birth control services to patients. At the same time this center affiliate, as we call it, as well as the other two types of affiliates educate the community in the appreciation of the importance of planned, responsible parenthood and helps its citizens gain awareness of the global population problem. A second type of affiliate is the action affiliate. It does not operate a center but trains lay workers to distribute simple, nonphysician birth control methods such as vaginal creams, suppositories, and intravaginal tablets to women in the surrounding areas. A third type is the educational affiliate, which offers no birth control but energizes and stimulates existing medical agencies in the community to provide full birth control services.

Data from the 1963 Annual Report will inform you of the work done by Planned Parenthood-World Population last year.

In the four-year period 1959 to 1963, the number of contraceptive patients served annually rose from 120,000 to 231,000. The 1963 patient volume increased 24 per cent over that of 1962.

This accelerated growth gives tangible evidence of the acceptability of oral contraception to the type of population served. Recently, I asked my friend Dudley Kirk how many women of reproductive age there were in the United States. He obligingly took out an envelope and pencil and quickly derived the figure 45 million.

Subtracting from this figure the unmarried, the subfertile, those who are pregnant, and those who are trying to become pregnant, we are left with perhaps 15 or 20 million married females who potentially might use contraception. On this basis, then, Planned Parenthood supplies birth control advice to between 1 and 1.5 per cent of the United States married market. It is impossible to calculate what proportion of the remainder require our services and do not get them. The 231,000 patients who we saw in 1963 made 697,000 visits during that year.

Sixty-eight per cent of the patients we served for birth control had total family incomes of less than $75 per week, that is, less than $3,850 per year. Thirty-six per cent are on welfare or have incomes of less than $50 per week.

Eighty per cent were under thirty years of age and 21 per cent were less than twenty years of age. Seventy per cent of the patients had three children or less.

In addition, we gave premarital or marriage counseling advice to 6,500 men and women; 5,400 couples sought help in our clinics for infertility.

What is the budget of Planned Parenthood-World Population compared to other voluntary health agencies?

In 1963 we raised $6,227,531, while the National Tuberculosis Association raised $30,000,000; Heart, $29,000,000; Cancer, $42,000,-000. Even Muscular Dystrophy raised $5.5 million.

Certainly no one would contest the observation that uncontrolled fertility affects more American women each year—when the number of induced abortions, illegitimate births, rejected or abandoned children, battered and unwanted babies are added together—than the number afflicted with all four illnesses listed above combined. Yet the financial support of Planned Parenthood-World Population is 5.8 per cent of the grand total collected by the four other health agencies mentioned above.

Of the $6 million raised by Planned Parenthood-World Population in 1963, approximately $3 million was donated to the 106 affiliates. They also received $1.75 million in patients' fees from those who could afford to pay.

This $4.75 million was all spent at the local level. Of the $1.25 million raised by National, $400,000 was given to International Planned Parenthood. This makes up 80 per cent of the total funds available to International Planned Parenthood.

The funds for Planned Parenthood-World Population were given by 79,000 individuals, a proportionately small number when compared to the numbers donating to other voluntary health agencies.

Planned Parenthood is operated by a lay Board of 100 men and women from all over the United States. The Board meets three times a year, and the Executive Committee of the Board meets monthly.

The professional staff at National Headquarters numbers sixty persons. They are divided between several departments: Medical (including Public Health), Social Research, Information and Education, Field, Future Development, Administrative and Fund Raising. The Medical and Social Research Divisions each has strong advisory committees recruited from experts in the two fields. The Field Department has a local office in each of six large geographic areas into which the country is divided. These are supervised by the field director and her assistant in New York. Field personnel are assigned to special groups such as migrants and Spanish-speaking Americans.

A word as to the future of the American movement: If Planned Parenthood succeeds in persuading governmental and other health agencies, such as voluntary hospitals, to take over completely their rightful task of supplying full and enthusiastic contraceptive services to all who desire them, we could and should close our clinics. If this time ever comes it would leave Planned Parenthood free to take over the task for which it is uniquely suited, to educate the public to appreciate fully the privileges and obligations of parenthood.

If the ideal of responsible parenthood were achieved, concentration on the quality rather than the quantity of population would be a natural result. Then Planned Parenthood would take on a different meaning. And I do not mean quality purely from the genetic point of view.

I would now like to discuss briefly the International Planned Parenthood Federation. Headquarters are located in London. The funds received are distributed between Headquarters and the five regional areas by a Budget and Finance Committee, which, in order to make United States contributions tax deductible, is composed only of Americans.

International is ruled by a Governing Body, each member country having membership on it. The Governing Body convenes every two years. Its executive committee, called the Management and Planning Committee, meets at least once a year. The president of the International is Lady Rama Rau of India; the chairman of the Management and Planning Committee is Mr. Cass Canfield of the United States.

The top-ranking professional is Sir Colville Deverell, the very recently appointed secretary general. There is an International Medical Committee of ten physicians which I have the honor to chair. There was a World Conference of International Planned Parenthood in

Singapore last year which many of you attended. It convenes every four years.

Our Western Hemisphere Region has six member countries in addition to the United States: Barbados, Bermuda, Canada, Jamaica, Puerto Rico, and Trinidad-Tobago. Despite the fact that there are no full members from mainland Latin America, much organized activity is beginning throughout that part of the American continent.

At the recent Western Hemisphere Regional Conference held in San Juan, Puerto Rico, twenty-nine Caribbean and American continental countries sent delegates or observers. Official representatives of the ministers of health came from fourteen of the South and Central American republics. Thanks to Mrs. Ofelia Mendoza, who is here, there are now nine countries in this area in which contraceptive services are available to some degree, obviously, almost token in some areas. These countries are Argentina, Brazil, Chile, Guatemala, El Salvador, Honduras, Mexico, Venezuela, and Uruguay.

To support these developing groups, to encourage yet other national groups, and to continue the work already firmly established, it is estimated that $342,000 is needed this year by the Western Hemisphere Region of International alone. However, unfortunately, only a little more than $100,000 will be available.

12

Recent Developments in Public Health Family Planning Programs in the United States

LESLIE CORSA, JR.

No responsible American health leader can be proud of public health efforts in the United States today in the field of population control. True, information concerning population change in this country is better than in most areas of the world and official health agencies produce the vital statistics involved. True, there is great concern to keep up with population growth, nowhere more apparent than in attempts to keep the ratios of hospital beds and doctors to people constant. True, some $5 million is being spent annually by the federal government for research on reproduction related to population control. True, most of the American people are aware of and use a variety of methods of birth control. True, we are witnessing a recent spurt of public health interest and activity in several areas of the country, but this started from such a low point that the total effect to date remains small.

In fact, far too few public health officials have recognized the powerful effects that population growth and distribution are having on all aspects of life in the United States; even fewer have realized that population growth is not inevitable and have moved to do something about it. There are some understandable reasons:

1. The effects are of dimensions new in human experience.

2. They are inter-related with many other changes in our life in ways not yet fully understood.

3. Long "incubation" periods (10–25–70 years) intervene between the event of a cohort of births and its ultimate effects upon society.

4. Birth control is still so controversial a subject that thought and discussion of it are limited, particularly by those who will be responsible for implementation of public action programs.

But these are no longer valid excuses for inaction, and there are signs that public health forces are finally facing the problems and some of the actions they can and should take.

The current demographic position and problems of the United States are well summarized by Donald Bogue in the 1963 American Assembly background papers published under the title, "The Population Dilemma," in *Too Many Americans* by Lincoln and Alice Day, by the Population Reference Bureau, and by others. The facts are familiar to most of you but bear brief repetition here.

1. The population of the United States is growing at a rate of 1.6 per cent per year or at least twice the rate of most European countries.

2. This increase is a sizable 3 million persons a year at present.

3. If present rates continue, children born today who live to age sixty-five will be part of a nation nearly three times as populous as today.

4. This growth is the result of a postwar baby boom that has continued as the result of rising family sizes, despite a shrinking number of women of prime childbearing age.

5. The first wave of the baby boom is now entering the reproductive span and threatens to initiate another spurt of population growth.

6. Irrespective of what happens to future birth rates, the prospects we face in the next decades as the babies of the boom continue to grow up are somewhat staggering: in high school graduates, a sudden and continuing increase of about 1 million each year as well as sizable increases in numbers of dropouts; in college enrollments, a tripling within twenty years which will strain facilities and faculties beyond reasonable limits; in the labor market, a virtual avalanche of young persons seeking jobs at the same time that automation operates to reduce them; an increase in the number of

unemployed by 1980 which, even at present rates, will be more than half as great as was experienced during the great depression of the thirties; housing for about 800,000 new households each year, water supplies, sewage disposal, smog control, freeways, urban transportation, hospitals, recreation areas—demand for all these facilities will dwarf present serious problems with all such public services that require tax support and larger government.

7. Present trends in population distribution are likely to continue: away from rural into urban and suburban areas; out of the northeast into Florida and the Gulf coast; out of everywhere to the west coast; with continuing deterioration and redevelopment of large urban centers.

8. Fertility rates are not equal in all population groups but are substantially higher among the lowest economic groups who rely largely upon the government for medical care, which usually excludes family planning.

9. Basic data on fertility desires and limitations and on knowledge and use of contraceptive methods by the American people are becoming increasingly available following the pioneering national sample survey of white married women under forty years of age reported in 1959 by Freedman, Whelpton, and Campbell.

10. With only 6 per cent of the world's population, we consume roughly half the world's annual production of nonrenewable resources.

The 1963 American Assembly and subsequent regional assemblies on the population dilemma called for greater concern by our national, state, and local governments with regard to our own population problems. They recommended:

1. Intensified investigation of our population trends and problems, including their long-range as well as their short-term implications.

2. Accelerated government-financed research on the biological and medical aspects of human reproduction, so that a variety of improved methods of fertility control can be developed.

3. Assumption of responsibility by the federal, state, and local governments for making available information concerning the regulation of fertility and providing services to needy mothers compatible

with the religious and ethical beliefs of the individual recipient. . . .

To accomplish these goals requires sizable new efforts by many groups, including official health agencies. What is actually happening?

Federal support of research on reproduction related to population control received considerable publicity over disagreements and delays in publication of a January, 1963, survey by the National Institutes of Health. The survey listed 758 projects costing $8.2 million during 1962, of which $5.2 million came from federal government sources. President Kennedy's press conference of April, 1963, establishment of the National Institute of Child Health and Human Development with specific responsibilities in this field, and the special report and recommendations of the National Academy of Sciences have all helped some to speed up needed biological, medical, and social research. However, to date, the increased federal effort appears to have been effectively countered by low salaries and economy drives which deter competent investigators from key jobs, and we are therefore fortunate that increased private resources are also at work. The contributions of the Milbank Memorial Fund, the Ford Foundation, the Population Council, and of schools of public health at Johns Hopkins, Harvard, California, Michigan, and Pittsburgh deserve special mention here.

After a long dormancy, we have now entered a period of change in the United States regarding the role of government in birth control services. A firm trend is developing no longer to deny birth control to persons receiving their medical care primarily from government facilities or funds. John Rock, in his recent book, *The Time Has Come*, reviews past religious controversy on these matters and states what he believes to be satisfactory ground rules for settling disputes over public policy in this field:

1. Family planning, whether by contraception or continence, is both a religious matter, involving the individual consciences of husbands and wives, and a medical problem, involving considerations of the health and well-being of families and, thus, of society.

2. The State has no competence—and no right—to legislate on the religious aspects of the problem.

3. In the medical programs operated by the State, however, proper medical care normally requires the provision of family planning services. In these programs, all restrictions on birth control, written or unwritten, should be removed.

4. In public facilities, no one should be compelled to accept birth control, or to participate in a birth control program, against his will.

5. All methods of family planning, including the rhythm method, should be offered so that the adherent of any faith will be able to choose a method that accords with his own conscience.

Such principles are slowly being adopted in practice in the United States. The first case to receive public attention was the 1958 dispute in New York City which ended in reversal of a long-standing policy denying contraceptive services to the poor and medically needy. In 1959 the American Public Health Association adopted a new and clear policy statement on population problems and on public health responsibilities for action. This was followed in the next few years by similar statements from other national bodies and from state organizations and official health agencies. The American Medical Association and state and local medical associations have given strong support. The U.S. Supreme Court is being asked to determine the constitutionality of restrictive laws in Connecticut (one of the two states still retaining such statutes) which have been challenged as unconstitutional in a test case initiated in 1961.* The federal government, except for its report on research, has remained notably silent and inactive regarding this domestic issue. The American Public Health Association is moving to fill the federal vacuum.

An American Public Health Association survey last summer of state and local health department services in family planning indicated that actual change in services was lagging far behind policy change. Seven states (Alabama, Florida, Georgia, Mississippi, North Carolina, South Carolina, and Virginia) have included family planning as a regular part of their public health services for about twenty-five years and continue to do so, operating a total of almost 500 clinics. There is little information available by which to evaluate these efforts. Only four additional states (California, Colorado, Kansas, and Maryland) reported that they now provide some family planning clinic services, and in a total of only 18 local health departments. In three of those same states and four others (Delaware, Illinois, Nebraska, and Texas), health departments also reported providing space and other assistance for private agency clinics. Certain referral and educational activities occur in a few other states, but there are an astonishing number of

* See footnote, Dr. Guttmacher's paper, p. 122.

zero's appearing in most categories in most states on the United States map portraying these family planning services in a current American Public Health Association exhibit. There are indications that the score will be significantly higher in a re-survey this summer, but it has a long, long way to go. These programs have all been developed as a part of maternal health programs of health departments and/or hospitals. They all require training of health department personnel.

A few words are in order about the developments that took place in California and Maryland, the two states in which the greatest change has so far occurred. The first significant step in California was unanimous adoption by the legally constituted Conference of Local Health Officers on October 26, 1961, of a policy on family planning which specified certain health department responsibilities, including the provision of family planning services for those groups who cannot reasonably obtain them. Several local health departments proceeded at once to implement this policy and others followed. During the 1963 Legislature a resolution on family planning as a health department function was widely discussed but was eventually referred to an interim committee, where it remains under study. A separate but somewhat related humane abortion law suffered the same fate. However, at the same time, in May, 1963, the Health and Welfare Agency Administrator issued a policy statement re-affirming health department responsibility and indicating need for expansion of family planning services. Strong supporting action has come from local Planned Parenthood Associations and from state and local medical associations on the basis that an adequate medical program should include family planning. In January, 1964, the State Board of Health, following similar action by the Conference of Local Health Officers three months earlier, adopted a recommendation on standards for state aid for local health administration which stated that local health departments should provide specified services in the field of family planning. At present nine departments provide clinical services directly, and an additional six provide these services through close arrangements with a private agency. Ten more counties have clinics in their county hospitals, and the numbers are increasing.

In Maryland, the most important single action was adoption on October 28, 1962, by the State Board of Public Welfare of a policy in favor of family planning for Aid to Dependent Children families; this was followed immediately by a State Department of Health recommendation that local health officers co-operate by making family planning services available. In the succeeding eighteen months sixteen of the twenty-four local health departments have developed family planning services within their health centers in areas covering 85 per cent of the population in Maryland.

Because of its unique relation to Congress, the government of the District of Columbia's initiation last month of a birth control program in its Department of Public Health is particularly noteworthy. This is essentially a pilot project available to clients of health and hospital clinics and of the Department of Public Welfare with an initial budget of $25,000, but may well be broadened at a later date to include many other women who could benefit from the service.

Prediction of social change in a controversial field is hazardous, but it seems safe to anticipate in the next few years:

1. Much more public discussion of all aspects of population growth.

2. Greater inclusion and evaluation of family planning services as part of medical care provided by government.

3. Accelerated laboratory and field biological and social research related to population control.

4. Improved and expanded graduate instruction on population problems and control, especially in schools of medicine and public health.

5. A salutary effect upon the United States' ability to provide technical assistance on population control to other countries that request it.

Such progress is predicated upon continued expansion of leadership in this field by public health workers of all kinds. Without this expansion nothing significant will happen. With it there is realistic hope that man will be able to meet the growing threat of too many births in the United States and elsewhere.

13

Epidemiology of
Provoked Abortion
in Santiago, Chile

ROLANDO ARMIJO AND TEGUALDA MONREAL *

Introduction

Abortion has been a matter of concern since an early era.[1] It is quite logical to assume that since those ancient times clandestine abortion has existed and that it has evidenced an upward trend, constituting nowadays a major health problem.[2]

The majority of studies carried out until now have been based on hospital material, which does not reflect what really happens in the community where abortion originates. Little is known about the nature and magnitude of such a problem or which are the most vulnerable groups in the female population or about the causes and other features describing the natural history of provoked abortion.

The use of the term "epidemiology of abortion" will seem inadequate to some people. Epidemiological occurrence can be defined as a logical chain of events which is determined by factors inherent in the host-agent-environment triad. Provoked abortion occurs voluntarily, that is, the phenomenon lacks self-determination. However, a complex series of ecological factors gravitate upon human decision which, as in the

* The authors wish to thank the Public Health Department of the Medical College for its financial contribution and enthusiastic support; the Fifth Zone of the National Health Service, and especially the team of Social Workers; the Department of Biostatistics of the School of Public Health for its constant advice; the Population Council for its technical advice and financial contribution; and finally the 1,890 women who disclosed so many important truths for the benefit of this epidemiological study.

case of homicide or suicide, admit the epidemiological analysis. The
nature of the present study, approaching abortion as a disease affecting
many women, appears to fit into this doctrine.

Abortion in Chile is illegal. In proven cases, the penalties are quite
severe for both the woman and the one who caused it, a situation which
renders any investigation most difficult.

Data from hospitals in the country show a steady increase of
admissions due to abortion, particularly during the last decades.
During a period of twenty-four years, the number of admissions
increased from 12,963 to 57,368. The number of hospital deliveries
increased 1.7 times, whereas the corresponding figure for abortions was
4.4. Consequently, in relation to the number of births, there was an
increase in abortions from 8.4 per 100 hospital births in 1937 to 22.3 per
100 births in 1960.

Romero and Vildosola (1952) interviewed 3,038 women admitted
to hospitals for delivery or abortion. According to their data, in 26.5
per cent of pregnancies the outcome would be abortion, and approximately two-thirds of these would be provoked abortions.[3]

Manubens (1952) found in a series of 1,000 hospitalized women that
approximately 1 abortion would occur per 2 deliveries, and two-thirds
of the abortions would be provoked.[4]

Mena (1952) studied a series of 1,000 abortions in four Obstetrical
Departments in Santiago and concluded that 52 per cent of them were
provoked.[5]

The fertility survey [6] carried out by the Latin American Centre of
Demography and the University of Chile School of Journalism (1959)
in urban (Greater) Santiago found a frequency of 1 abortion per 3
live births in women from broken homes or living in free union.

Plaza and Briones [7] carried out a study (1962) on abortion as a
medical care problem in four general hospitals and four Emergency
Departments in Santiago and in five general hospitals in various
provinces. Among other conclusions they reached, we wish to stress the
following:

1. Abortion accounted for 8.1 per cent of all admissions to hospitals
   run by the National Health Service.

2. Per each 100 deliveries, 24.3 abortion cases were admitted in Santiago and 34.3 to the provincial hospitals. This shows the number of obstetrical beds which are being occupied by abortion cases.

3. Abortion alone accounted for 35 per cent of all surgical operations
   performed in some of the Emergency Departments surveyed. (In

one case, 78 per cent of all surgical operations consisted of uterine curettage.)

4. Abortion accounted for 17.7 per cent of all blood transfusions and 26.7 per cent of the total blood volume dispensed in Emergency Departments in Santiago.

The damage and economic loss produced by abortion are most difficult to evaluate. The case fatality rate in hospitals oscillated around 5 per 1,000, more than double that of maternal mortality. The consequences and complications, both immediate and late, comprise a wide range of pathological and psychological disturbances.

With regard to economic loss, the National Health Service is spending in hospital care of abortion patients a large amount, which is hard to determine. In one single year, 1960, the care of 57,368 abortions meant a total of nearly 184,000 bed-days, involving an expense of well over $1 million. Plaza and Briones determined in complicated cases (sepsis *C. perfringens*) that one single survivor would cost around $3,000.

The preceding data are enough to demonstrate that in Chile abortion represents a major health problem deserving priority for the purpose of study and control.

Objectives

The over-all objectives of this study have been oriented in three major directions:

1. To define the magnitude and most relevant features of provoked abortion and the variables associated with it as etiological factors.

2. To explore in the female population attitudes relating to family planning and the use of contraceptives.

3. To explore habits and attitudes relating to the female intimate life.

Method of Sampling

The aim has been to interview, through home visits, a random sample of women in the twenty to forty-four year age group living in urban Santiago.

The first step consisted, consequently, in deciding on the universe from which the sample was to be taken. The last 1960 census comprises in urban Santiago twelve municipalities with a total female population of 1,019,291.

Once the total figure was known, the next step consisted in ascertaining the proportion of women in the twenty to forty-four year age group. Unfortunately, this information could not be obtained from the existing data because of incomplete tabulation. The alternate source of information was the 1952 census, which showed that approximately 40 per cent of all women fell in this age group. A certain degree of error having been allowed for, by applying this proportion to the figure encountered in the 1960 census, it was estimated that our universe should amount to nearly 407,000 women in the twenty to forty-four year age group.

According to the best estimates, and taking into account the available resources, it was found that a sample involving 2,000 dwellings would be enough for the purpose of our study. An average of 1.25 women eligible for the study per dwelling could be expected, making a total of approximately 2,500 women. If a 20 per cent loss (wrong addresses, nonco-operation, demolished houses, etc.) was allowed for, it could be expected finally to reach around 2,000 women.

The second stage consisted in designing a model in order to select the census zones within the districts of each municipality. A census zone was chosen as the primary unit for the purpose of sampling. It can be defined as the geographic area which one single worker can cover in one day. In general, a census zone, the size of which varies according to the population density, comprises between twenty and fifty dwellings. It was decided that within each census zone a fixed number of six house units should be taken. The procedure would allow equal chances to a larger number of zones, in order to avoid concentrating the sample in heavily populated districts of the city.

It was necessary to find a population segment or "space," irrespective of the size of the census zone.

Each census zone was allowed a probability of being selected proportional to the number of women in the twenty to forty-four year age group found by the census. Since the specific female population of urban Santiago was estimated as 407,851, and since it was expected to obtain a sample of 2,500, the expected relative size should be:

$$f = \frac{2,500}{407,851} = 6 \text{ per thousand}$$

In order to choose the census zones, a linear distribution of all the 1,019,291 women was assumed. Since it had been decided to take six dwellings out of each census zone, the division of 2,500 units by six would give the number of population segments:

$$\frac{2,500}{6} = 416 \text{ segments}$$

Going back to the linear distribution of the total female population, each one of the 416 segments should comprise 2,450 women of all ages, since

$$\frac{1,019,291}{416} = 2,450$$

Within each segment, a woman was selected at random on the assumption that every woman indicates a position in the series and, therefore, a home unit. Of the series of numbers between 1 and 2,450, a chance procedure came out with the figure 2,213. This figure served to individualize one woman and therefore one dwelling or family unit leading up to a census zone. In the series of 1,019,291 women of all ages, it served us both as the starting point and the population "space." The municipalities were arranged by districts and these by census zones, each one indicated by the female population in a linear fashion. A simple procedure of successive subtraction of the figure encountered by chance (2,213) enabled us to build up a sample consisting of 414 census zones, uniformly distributed throughout urban Santiago.

Once the 414 census zones had been identified in the records, six dwellings were taken out of each zone. Collective dwellings such as hospitals, army quarters, and the like were left out.

In this way a random sample of 2,468 dwellings was established. An average number of seventy home units was allotted to each one of the thirty-five social workers who were ready to start visiting the homes.

Procedure

Provoked abortion is a problem of such an emotional nature and of such human and social complexity that the experience achieved in this study may be helpful to other workers. And this is why the procedure is described in some detail.

The nature of the study and the type of data to be collected having been considered, it was decided that the most suitable procedure should be the house-to-house inquiry done by specially selected social workers. It was decided that the social worker appeared to be the most adequate field agent for this study because:

1. They constitute a professional group recognized by the Chilean population since they were the first paramedical workers ever developed in Chile.

2. Social workers are trained particularly in surveys similar to the one in view, so that they have developed an ability to appraise and investigate data on income, salary, rent, and the like.

3. Social workers were more readily available than nurses, midwives, etc.

A suitable questionnaire form was discussed and tried out among mothers attending a maternal and child clinic, where it proved to be satisfactory. Since most delicate matters had to be touched on, it was carefully designed so as to start with simple questions, getting slowly into the obstetrical and sexual matters as the interviewer gained the confidence of the woman. It was found that following this line it was easier to get the history of abortions than data on the family income.

The women were so eager to find an escape for their constantly suppressed anxieties about the menstrual cycles, delays, pregnancies, and abortions that the survey became a far easier task than had been expected. Moreover, many of the women became deeply interested in the results of the study and worked hard to furnish the information to the best of their knowledge. The average time per complete interview was 45 minutes. In a few cases (2.7 per cent of frank refusals) where the social workers failed, the women interviewed were mostly spinsters who had no interest in this inquiry.

It was necessary to select the most experienced, alert, and conscientious social workers. One of us spent a number of sessions with the thirty-five chosen, in order to discuss thoroughly the matter in question. Only after the group was keenly interested in the problem and after the directions for recording each answer had been fully understood was it decided that the time had come to start the field work.

In addition to the previous training, each social worker was given an annex with written instructions for the proper use of the form. In order to avoid any difficulty when visiting the homes, a credential card was given to them, signed by the director of the School of Public Health, which proved to be quite useful. Each social worker received what was called a "route slip," which contained the addresses of the homes to be visited.

A number of periodical meetings was necessary in order to discuss the day-to-day news and to keep up with a uniform procedure throughout the whole survey. It was decided that any woman in the twenty to forty-four year age group could be interviewed. It was thought that the age group fifteen to nineteen, although very interesting to investigate, was too difficult to interview because of untrustworthy replies. At the other end, the age group forty-five to forty-nine, because of reduced fertility, seemed to be scarcely worthwhile. Nevertheless it was very difficult to avoid the inclusion of a certain number of women in these age groups; some of them got in by mistake and others specially requested inclusion.

Repeated calls were made if the woman was absent on the first visit. Only outdoor servants were excluded, since the sampling definition had been made with respect to domicile and not the place of work.

Santiago is divided into five health areas. In each area a senior social worker was responsible for supervision and collection of the complete forms, which were gradually relayed to one of us in the School of Public Health for revision and filing. In this way the central investigator kept in close contact with the whole field operation.

A code was prepared in order to transfer the data to punch cards. It was necessary to arrange two sets of cards: one to record the characteristics of the women and the other for the attributes of every provoked abortion.

Tabulation of the data resulted in a much more difficult task than ordinary work because of the various qualitative questions which required constant revision for proper interpretation. Adjusting the abortions to the age at the moment of occurrence, civil status, number of living children, and other dynamic variables was a tremendous job. Therefore, it was necessary to go back constantly to the original records. In other words, the material consisting of 1,890 women and 1,394 provoked abortions admitted became, with the abundance of data, a very rich source for retrospective analysis. This involved patient cross-analysis and rearrangement of data, which took over a year.

Results

This report agrees and confirms to a large extent the findings given in our interim report.[8-9] According to the objectives of this study, the results are described with respect to the characteristics of the women interviewed and the epidemiological description of provoked abortion. The discussion on the female intimate life and the exploration of attitudes relating to family planning are restricted to a summary of the most relevant findings.

CHARACTERISTICS OF THE WOMEN INTERVIEWED

The distribution characteristics of the 1,890 women correspond fairly well to the characteristics known or expected in the over-all universe. The five health areas of greater Santiago were evenly represented. Sixty-eight per cent of the dwellings selected could be surveyed, the proportion ranging between 62.6 and 73.8 per cent.

Seventy-one women under twenty years of age (mainly eighteen and nineteen) and 110 in the forty-five to forty-nine year age group were nevertheless included in the study. The majority of women interviewed were married (71.5 per cent) and only 16.2 per cent were single.

Five per cent of the women were illiterate, a proportion falling within what could be expected in urban Santiago. At the other extreme, 2 per cent had reached university level. Seventy-three per cent were engaged in housekeeping. As for the rest, the picture depicts the situation of the female population in a developing country, including employees, industrial workers, self-employed, and servants.

The sample shows slightly greater proportions of women in the thirty to thirty-four year age group, of married women, and housewives as compared with data obtained from the census. However, it is considered that these minor deviations do not affect the results. The social and economic level of the population surveyed was predominantly low. Eighty-two per cent live on less than two vital salaries, and 69.6 per cent fall in the lowest social categories. At the other extreme, 8.5 per cent of those studied live on three or more vital salaries, whereas 8.8 per cent falls into the upper social groups. The high degree of socialized medicine existing in Chile can be noted. Sixty-five per cent of the women are distributed according to a variety of systems, predominantly the Social Insurance Fund, which means full coverage by the National Health Service.

EPIDEMIOLOGICAL DESCRIPTION OF PROVOKED ABORTION

Incidence. The figures obtained are the result of interviews made by social workers. Error is more likely to occur in the direction of deficiency rather than excess in reporting. Therefore, this factor must

TABLE 1: SUMMARY OF 1,890 WOMEN REGARDING HISTORY OF
ABORTION, SANTIAGO, 1962

	All Abortions	Provoked Abortions
Number of women with history of abortion	875	496
Per cent	46.3	26.2
Total number of abortions reported	2,212	1,394
Average number of abortions per woman	2.5	2.8

be borne in mind when the figures given below are interpreted.

Forty-six per cent of the women admitted a positive history of abortion, making a total of 2,212 abortions of any kind, and 26 per cent (496) admitted a definite history of one or more provoked abortions (Table 1). These 496 women had had 1,394 provoked abortions in all. Figure 1 shows that the majority had had up to 3 provoked abortions,

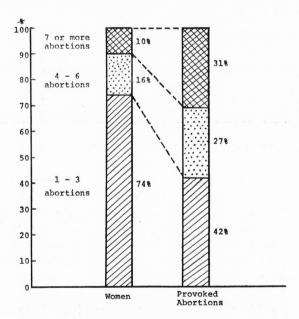

Figure 1. Per cent distribution of the women according to the number of provoked abortions, Santiago, 1962.

accounting for 42 per cent of the 1,394 cases. However, one-fourth of the women accounted for 58 per cent, and 10 per cent of the women were responsible for one-third of the provoked abortions. Fifteen women who had had 187 abortions accounted for 13 per cent of the total. The existence of women resorting to abortion repeatedly has practical importance for prevention. Women between twenty and thirty-four years of age accounted for 85.6 per cent of the provoked abortions. The distribution was arranged according to the age at the moment of occurrence. This retrospective arrangement allowed us to speculate on the possibility of figuring out a cohort, assuming that each woman had been followed up since the age of fifteen. On this assump-

TABLE 2: INCIDENCE OF PROVOKED ABORTION BY AGE GROUP, ACCORDING TO
RETROSPECTIVE ANALYSIS, IN 1,890 WOMEN QUESTIONED, SANTIAGO, 1962
(RATES PER 100 WOMEN)

Age at Abortion	No. of Women Theoretically Observed	No. of Provoked Abortions	5-Year Rate	Annual Rate
Under 20	1,855	94	5.1	1.0
20–24	1,666	373	22.4	4.5
25–29	1,327	440	33.1	6.6
30–34	930	296	31.9	6.4
35–39	548	79	14.4	2.9
40–44	243	12	4.9	1.0
45 and over	55	2	3.6	0.7
Ignored	—	98	—	—

tion, of the 1,890 women, 1,855 had already passed the lowest age group and they had therefore theoretically been observed for periods up to twenty-five years; 1,666 had passed the twenty to twenty-four year age period, subject to the same criterion of theoretical observation, and so on. These figures were used as denominators for the abortions enumerated by age of occurrence. This is shown in Table 2.

The rate for those under twenty appears markedly low, and its reliability is questionable. Apart from this group, the remaining five-year and annual rates are consistent in showing that the incidence of provoked abortion is highest in the twenty-five to twenty-nine year age group, followed by the thirty to thirty-four and twenty to twenty-four age groups.

As the most recent abortions may be kept in mind more easily than those which occurred in the past, the study was focused on 1961, that is, the year prior to the questioning. The total number of abortions recorded was 165, of which 82 were provoked abortions. The distribution and rate by age is shown in Figure 2. In the single year 1961 the over-all incidence was 4.2 per 100 women, with a peak for women in the twenty-five to twenty-nine and thirty to thirty-four year age groups. The annual incidence rates found for 1961 compare quite well with those found in Table 2.

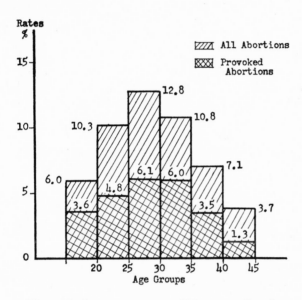

Figure 2. One-year rate per 100 women for abortions by age, Santiago, 1962.

Estimates of the number of abortions. Assuming that our sample was representative of all women of reproductive age in Santiago, and applying the rates found above, we could estimate the expected number of provoked abortions for 1962, which amounted to 24,930; for all abortions, regardless of their type, the expected number was 49,614.

After analysis of the relationship between births and abortions, the data were separated for the decade 1952–61 and for the single year 1961 (Table 3). It can be seen that the ratios found compare quite well.

By applying the ratios to the number of births recorded in 1962, we

TABLE 3: NUMBER OF BIRTHS, ALL ABORTIONS, PROVOKED
ABORTIONS, AND RATIOS OF ABORTIONS TO BIRTHS FOUND
IN THE SAMPLE, SANTIAGO, 1952–61 AND 1961

	1952–61	1961
Births	3,267	362
All abortions	1,310	165
Provoked abortions	762	82
Ratios per 100 live births:		
All abortions	40.1	45.6
Provoked abortions	23.3	22.6

arrived at the following figures: all abortions, 35,276; provoked abortions, 17,483. The figures resulting from this method appear lower than those given before.

A third approach consisted in determining the proportion of cases with and without a history of hospital admission. Once the second proportion was found it was possible to estimate the number of abortions. Figure 3 shows that 58 per cent of all abortions and 68 per cent of provoked abortions had no history of hospital admission.

In 1960, 18,240 cases of abortion of all types were admitted to hospitals in Santiago. If it is assumed that this represents 41.6 per cent of abortions occurring in the city, the real over-all figure should be 43,845 for that year, which compares with the above estimate based on the rates (49,614 for the year 1962).

Civil status and parity. Since a number of women had a history of multiple provoked abortions, each instance had to be revised retro-

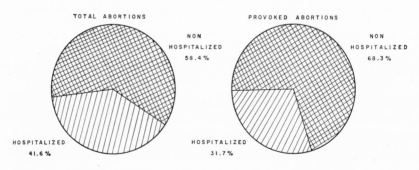

Figure 3. Distribution of abortions according to hospital admission, Santiago, 1962.

spectively in order to determine the civil status when the abortion occurred. Seventy-one per cent of the women were married and accounted for 85 per cent of the provoked abortions, whereas single women contributed only 8.4 per cent of them. The rates found for 1961 per 100 women, were as follows:

Married or concubine	4.9
Widow or separated	3.0
Single	1.9

If this is true, the problem of provoked abortion is affecting mostly married women and concubines who are constantly exposed to the risk.

Living children. Seventy-seven per cent of the provoked abortions were (Figure 4) concentrated in women who had three or fewer children alive (5 per cent had no children). There is a common trend among obstetricians to stress education and help, even sterilization, for women who have a large number of children. Meantime, very little or no attention is paid to women who have less than four children, precisely those who, according to these findings, are contributing most of the provoked abortions.

Social bracket. Analyzing abortion in relation to social bracket and considering only data for 1961, one observes that abortion was practiced at all levels. The rate adjusted for age oscillates between 5.4 per 100 women in the upper class to 10.2 in the lowest. The social bracket appears to have a definite bearing on birth, infant mortality, and abortion rates, as is shown in Figure 5 (rates adjusted by age).

Order of pregnancy. Provoked abortions appear to be concentrated in women with up to six pregnancies, with the highest frequency for the fourth, fifth, and sixth pregnancies. With respect to the month of gestation, 98 per cent of provoked abortions appear to occur within the first three months.

The person provoking the abortion and the method used. If the abortions induced by physicians (11.5 per cent) are left out, most interruptions were made by nonqualified persons (Table 4). Particular attention should be paid to abortions induced by the women themselves and by amateur midwives (38.3 per cent), which have the highest incidence of infection, hemorrhage, and other complications. Graduate midwives, who make a nice income out of abortion, are generally reliable.

The insertion of a rubber tube into the cervix appears to be the most

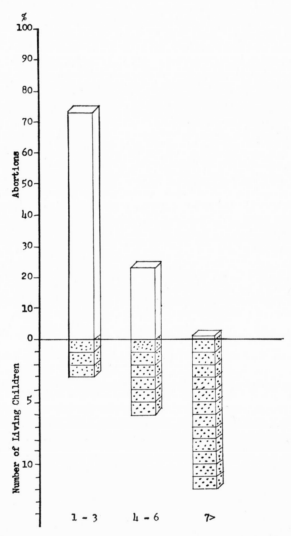

Figure 4. Per cent distribution of 1,394 provoked
abortions according to the number of living children
at the moment of occurrence, Santiago, 1962.

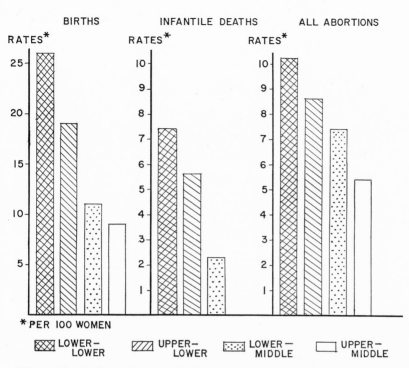

Figure 5. Births, infantile deaths, and abortions according to social bracket, Santiago, 1962.

popular method for provoking abortion (46.1 per cent). The item "others" includes, for example, the insertion of a parsley stem into the cervix.

Participation of the marital partner. Nearly 74 per cent of the abortions had been approved by the marital partner. This finding

TABLE 4: DISTRIBUTION OF 1,394 PROVOKED ABORTIONS BY PERSON PROVOKING THE ABORTION, SANTIAGO, 1962

Person	Number of Abortions	Per Cent
Graduate midwife	638	50.3
Amateur midwife	344	27.3
Physician	146	11.5
Self-induced	139	11.0
No data	127	—
	1,394	100

points to an interesting pattern of communication between the couple, showing that four out of five times this delicate problem was discussed with the marital partner, which strongly suggests that an abortion prevention program should involve the male.

Causes of abortion claimed by the women. Causes of abortion are shown in Figure 6, stressing the importance of economic reasons.

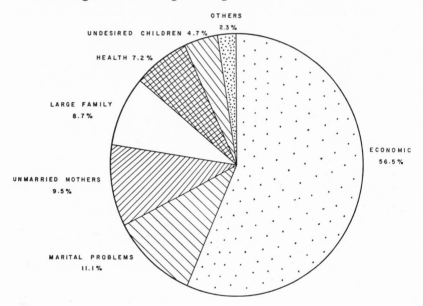

Figure 6. Distribution of 1,394 provoked abortions according to causes claimed by the women, Santiago, 1962.

Opinions of the Women on Family Planning

Seventy-four per cent of the women were in favor of family planning (Table 5). Financial considerations were the chief reasons given by those favoring planned parenthood. The remaining 26 per cent objected on religious grounds. However, a closer analysis showed that the real proportion opposing all methods of limitation did not exceed 15 per cent. A similar proportion of women (71.3 per cent) were openly in favor of the legalization of abortion.

Use of Contraceptives

Of 1,501 exposed women, less than one-third was using some type of contraceptives, most of them not reliable (Figure 7). Here the study

TABLE 5: OPINIONS OF 1,890 WOMEN INTERVIEWED
ON FAMILY PLANNING, WITH SUPPORTING REASONS,
SANTIAGO, 1962

	Number	Per Cent
Positive answers	1,402	74.2
Reasons:		
Economic	1,077	
Not specified	156	
Economic-health	54	
Large family	34	
Unmarried mother	27	
Health	24	
Conjugal problems	17	
Others	13	
Negative answers	465	24.6
No opinion	23	1.2
	1,890	100

faces the ultimate cause of provoked abortion, that is, the ignorance of
prevention procedures by a mass of women who are under constant
exposure.

Table 6 shows an inverse relationship between social bracket and use

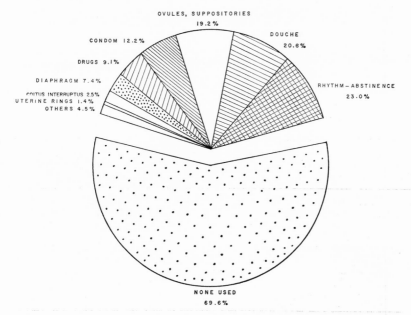

Figure 7. Use of contraceptives by the exposed women, Santiago, 1962.

TABLE 6: USE OF CONTRACEPTIVES AMONG 1,501 SEXUALLY
EXPOSED WOMEN BY SOCIAL BRACKET, SANTIAGO, 1962

Social Bracket	Number Exposed	Number Using Contraceptives	Per Cent
Upper and upper-middle	124	70	56.4
Lower-middle	322	162	50.5
Upper-lower	497	199	40.0
Lower-lower	558	126	22.6
Total	1,501	557	37.1

of contraceptives, providing additional support to the fact that women
in the low income groups are in greater need of advice and help for
prevention of abortions.

The contraceptives in use are shown in relation to social bracket in
Table 7. A variety of patterns can be noticed. For example, the diaphragm appears to be more widely used by women who can afford to
buy it; on the other hand, the douche is very popular in the low income
groups. Anyhow, the effectiveness of the procedures is quite questionable. The item "others" includes oral aspirin, micturition after coitus,
etc.

With respect to age, the proportion of women using contraceptives
appears somewhat higher in the twenty-five to twenty-nine and thirty
to thirty-four year age groups.

TABLE 7: TYPE OF CONTRACEPTIVES USED BY 557 WOMEN
ACCORDING TO SOCIAL BRACKET, SANTIAGO, 1962
(PERCENTAGES)

Contraceptives	Upper and Upper-Middle (70)	Lower-Middle (162)	Upper-Lower (199)	Lower-Lower (126)	All Women (557)
Abstinence	41.4	32.1	18.1	12.7	23.6
Douche	8.6	10.5	27.6	27.0	20.1
Ovules-suppositories	11.4	21.6	20.1	21.4	19.7
Condoms	15.7	11.1	11.6	11.9	11.8
Drugs	2.8	10.5	7.0	15.0	9.3
Diaphragms	14.3	9.9	4.5	1.6	6.6
Coitus interruptus	2.8	1.2	2.5	3.2	2.3
Others	2.8	3.0	7.5	7.1	5.6
Not specified	—	—	1.0	—	0.3

THE FEMALE INTIMATE LIFE

Eighty-five per cent of the women admitted to having had sexual experience. Of those sexually active, 52 per cent had their first intercourse under the age twenty. Retrospective analysis demonstrates a trend in which sexual initiation has been moving consistently to younger ages. In the sample studied, by 1930 only 28.1 per cent of women under twenty initiated their sexual life. Thirty years later, the proportion rises to 65.7 per cent. Sexual exposure and initiation appear closely associated with the social bracket, as shown in Table 8. The low

TABLE 8: PER CENT DISTRIBUTION BY SOCIAL BRACKET OF 1,890 WOMEN, ACCORDING TO SEXUAL EXPOSURE AND AGE AT FIRST INTERCOURSE, SANTIAGO, 1962

Sexual Exposure	Upper and Upper-Middle (166)	Lower-Middle (409)	Upper-Lower (657)	Lower-Lower (658)	All Women (1,890)
No exposure	10.8	8.8	11.1	4.9	8.4
First intercourse at:					
Under 20	24.7	36.2	40.6	56.4	43.8
20–24	35.5	32.8	29.1	23.4	20.4
25–29	13.2	10.5	10.3	7.6	9.7
30 and over	5.4	5.1	2.6	1.8	3.1
No answer	10.2	6.6	6.3	5.8	6.6

income groups start at an earlier age, another indication that a priority should be given to these groups in our consideration of the problems. While 56.4 per cent of the women in the lower-lower social bracket had their sexual initiation under 20, only 24.7 per cent did so in the upper social groups. The majority of women reported that they had sexual intercourse frequently enough to justify any measure aimed at abortion prevention (Figure 8).

This frequency appears to be associated with social bracket, as shown in Table 9. The low income groups appear to have relations slightly less frequently than the upper social groups.

Summary

The present investigation, begun at the end of 1961, had as its prime objective a contribution to the better knowledge of provoked abortion.

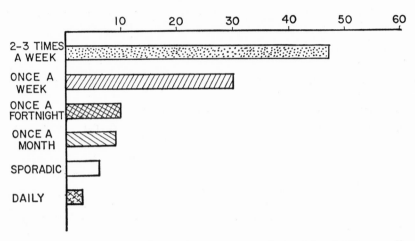

Figure 8. Frequency of sexual intercourse admitted by 1,133 sexually active women, Santiago, 1962.

By using the data from the 1960 census and by a laborious method, it was possible to draw a random sample of 2,464 dwellings in greater urban Santiago.

The National Health Service contributed a team of thirty-five social workers who made the house-to-house visits. The nature of the problem and the method of approach used involved lengthy planning and execution. Only 2.7 per cent of the homes remained outside the investigation because of lack of co-operation.

An account is given of the results obtained from the interviewing of a total of 1,890 women, who were almost entirely from twenty to forty-four years of age. The sample has been analyzed in its distribution characteristics, and we think that it represents the geographical whole.

Forty-six per cent of the women gave a positive history of abortion, making a total of 2,212 abortions of any kind. Twenty-six per cent (496 women) admitted a history of provoked abortion, giving a total of 1,394 provoked abortions.

The majority of women had had up to three provoked abortions, accounting for 42 per cent of the total. However, one-fourth of the women accounted for 58 per cent, and 10 per cent of the women were

TABLE 9: FREQUENCY OF SEXUAL INTERCOURSE AMONG 1,890
WOMEN BY SOCIAL BRACKET (PER CENT DISTRIBUTION)
SANTIAGO, 1961

Sexual Activity	Upper and Upper-Middle (166)	Lower-Middle (409)	Upper-Lower (657)	Lower-Lower (658)	All Women (1,890)
No sexual life	15.6	15.1	13.9	9.7	12.9
Daily or 2–3 times a week	30.1	30.5	26.4	28.1	28.2
Weekly-fortnightly	23.4	22.0	22.3	24.4	23.1
Monthly or sporadic	2.4	4.9	9.9	11.1	8.5
Not specified	9.0	13.4	11.6	10.8	11.4
No answer	19.2	13.9	15.8	15.8	15.7

responsible for one-third of the provoked abortions.

The highest incidence was noted among women between twenty and thirty-four years of age, who accounted for 86 per cent of the provoked abortions.

The rates were computed retrospectively, arranging the figures by age at the moment of occurrence. The rates computed for one single year, 1961, agree with data obtained retrospectively. By applying the 1961 rates to the female population it was possible to estimate the number of abortions occurring in Santiago as around 49,000.

Two other methods of approach were used in order to estimate the number of abortions. One consisted in studying the ratio between births and abortions found in the sample for the decade 1952–61 and for the year 1961. The figures obtained were somewhat lower than those obtained from the application of rates. The third method consists in determining the proportion of abortions without history of hospital admission. Fifty-six per cent of all abortions and 68 per cent of provoked abortions had evolved outside the hospital. By extrapolating these proportions to the number of hospital admissions known in Santiago, it was also possible to get an estimate of nearly 44,000 abortions.

A concentration of provoked abortions was found among married women and concubines. Seventy-seven per cent concentrated in women who had up to three children, a fact worthy of attention.

The social bracket shows a definite bearing on birth, infant mortality, and abortion rates. A marked inverse correlation was found for the year 1961, in which the low income groups had the highest rates.

Provoked abortions in relation to the pregnancy order showed a greater frequency between the fourth and the sixth; with regard to the month of gestation, the second month predominated.

In 50 per cent of cases the person provoking the abortion was the graduate midwife, followed by the amateur and finally by the doctor and the woman herself. The method used most often was the rubber tube.

In 80 per cent of cases the marital partner was consulted, and the majority of them approved the provoked abortion. Among the reasons given for abortion, economy predominated, regardless of the social bracket.

With regard to the exploration on family planning and on the use of contraceptives, it was found that 74 per cent of the women were in favor of family limitation, the majority for economic reasons. Seventy-one per cent considered that actual legislation should be modified in the sense that abortion should be authorized in certain circumstances. Twenty-nine per cent of the women admitted the use of some kind of contraceptive procedure, and the figure rises to 37 per cent when exposed women only were considered. The highest proportion of contraceptors was found among women from twenty-five to thirty-nine years of age. It is the better-off women (55 per cent) who make use of preventive methods, chiefly abstinence, condoms, and diaphragms. Lower-class women, only 23 per cent of whom use preventive methods, prefer douche and suppositories.

Finally as to the sexual life, if only the women with experience are considered, 52 per cent had their first intercourse under the age of twenty. Analysis of the trend in the beginning of sexual life made retrospectively shows an increasing proportion of those who start having intercourse before the age of twenty. With regard to frequency, almost half the women sexually active had intercourse two, three, or more times a week.

Conclusions

The study points to the following epidemiological features of provoked abortion in Santiago:

1. Recognition of provoked abortion as an increasing health problem: 26 per cent of women of reproductive age admitted a positive history of provoked abortion. The size of the problem exceeds by far what is officially known.

2. Recognition of the existence of vulnerable groups: the twenty to thirty-four year age group and a small proportion of women exposed to repeated abortions, the latter accounting for one-third of the total number recorded. Concentration of provoked abortions in married women, those having up to three children, and the low income groups. Most of the abortions are being provoked by nonqualified persons, who use risky methods which involve a serious danger.

3. Economic reasons and ignorance of birth control methods appear to be the basic explanations for the alarming upward trend of provoked abortion.

4. The majority of women as well as of marital partners are in favor of family planning and anxious to find a solution to their problem.

5. Sexual life starts earlier in the low income groups, and a retrospective analysis shows a trend toward earlier initiation of sexual experience in all social brackets. Sexual intercourse appears frequent; therefore exposure is constant for the majority of women.

Thus, there is need for efforts to prevent provoked abortion; priority should be given to the vulnerable groups described in this study. At present, abortion constitutes the worst method of family limitation. It appears mandatory to accomplish its replacement by contraceptive procedures. Furthermore, the evidence shown by the study points to the need for reviewing the present legislation.

The results of this study are being confirmed in other Latin American countries. If that is the case, the authors wish to stress the need for a realistic program of provoked abortion prevention.

References for Paper 13

1. Monreal, Tegualda, El Aborto Provocado: Síntesis Bibliograficá reciente, with a list of references. *Cuad. Med. Soc.*, Vol. II, No. 2, pp. 22–28.
2. Venning, G. R., The Abortion Problem. *Family Planning* (in press), 1964, with a list of references.
3. Romero, H. and Vildosola, J., Introducción al Problema del Aborto. *Rev. Ch. Hig. Med. Prev.*, Vol. 14, pp. 197–211.
4. Manubens, R., Estudio sobre aborto involuntario. Tesis U. de Ch. 1952.

5. Mena, V., Estudio sobre aborto provocado. Tesis U. de Ch. 1952.
6. Tabah, L. and Samuel, R., Encuesta de fecundidad y actitudes relativas a la formación de la familia, resultados preliminares. *Cuad. Med. Soc.*, Vol. II, No. 2, pp. 19–21.
7. Plaza, S. and Briones, H., El aborto como problema asistencial. *Rev. Med. Ch.*, Vol. 91, pp. 294–97.
8. Armijo, R. and Monreal, T., Epidemiology of Provoked Abortion in Santiago, Interim Report. *Eugenics Review*, Vol. 55, No. 1, pp. 32–33.
9. Armijo, R. and Monreal, T., Epidemiología del Aborto en Santiago. Informe preliminar presentado ante VII Congreso Médico-Social Panamericano. Santiago de Chile, 1962, *Rev. Conf. Med. Panam.*, Vol. 10, pp. 221–24.

14

Survey Research
and Population Control
in Latin America

J. MAYONE STYCOS *

Although various studies of human fertility were conducted on special populations in the United States earlier in the century, the Puerto Rican survey directed by Paul Hatt in 1948 was the first major effort outside the continental U.S. and probably the first representative sample of a total political unit with respect to fertility.[1] The study, utilizing traditional public opinion methodology, asked untraditional questions, such as the frequency of sexual relations and details of each pregnancy.

Throughout the fifties the number of such studies increased even faster than the population and began to include questions on knowledge and use of birth control. Within a decade such studies became so common that they have recently achieved the distinction of "Initial Nomenclature." In the profession they are now referred to as AUK studies—attitude, use and knowledge. Even demographers, an austere clan traditionally hostile toward soft data, have begun to admit the possible utility of AUK type data. Whelpton's recent population projections for the U.S. represent a landmark in demography, since for the first time in history they include couple's intentions about family size.[2]

*This paper was originally published in The Public Opinion Quarterly and is reprinted here, with minor changes, by the kind permission of the publisher.
[1] P. K. Hatt, Backgrounds of Human Fertility in Puerto Rico (Princeton: Princeton University Press, 1952).
[2] R. Freedman, P. K. Whelpton, and A. A. Campbell, Family Planning, Sterility and Population Growth (New York: McGraw-Hill, 1959).

What purposes are served by such studies in Latin America?

1. They serve the cause of social science generally by demonstrating that social and physiological facts can be collected and interpreted scientifically. While any successful social survey might do the same, the AUK is especially effective, for it deals with subject matter generally believed accessible only within the confessional. Thus, it is a *dramatic* demonstration of the scope and flexibility of the social survey. In country after country we have been told, "It can't be done here. Our people will not answer such questions." Of course, when it is done, there is considerable incredulity. "Yes, they answered your questions, but did they tell the *truth?*" For this reason it is especially important to build in reliability and validity checks.

2. The most important function of such surveys is similar to any market research project: to demonstrate the existence of a demand for goods or services, in this case for birth control. This may seem unnecessary or irrelevant in underdeveloped areas where excessive childbearing is only too obvious. But the elite in most societies believe that their people have many children because they want many children. They believe there are deep-seated psychological drives to demonstrate fertility, pervasive cultural and religious norms encouraging maximum childbearing, obsessive sexual patterns, and economic ideologies for the large family. They believe that to run counter to such a profound array of beliefs, drives, behavior patterns, and norms would either be political suicide or a waste of time. And indeed, they would be correct if such assumptions were true. But repeatedly surveys demonstrate that couples want a moderate number of children, that they are convinced of the economic disadvantages of a large family, and that they are eager for information on what to do about it. Such information, if believed, can show that a program of population control could win votes rather than lose them.

3. A third function of such studies relates to the fact that research is a relatively noncontroversial way of initiating activity in population control in countries where direct efforts are not possible. The research itself, in addition to providing valuable information for possible future programs, stimulates the interest of those directly and indirectly involved and may serve to accelerate the whole process of policy formation.

In Jamaica, e.g., where a narrow balance of power exists between two political parties, both parties were unwilling to sponsor a population control program for fear the opposition would use it against them;

but it *was* possible to get agreement on action oriented research and to form a sponsoring board for the research which included representation from both sides.

In Latin America, the liberal wing of the church is most eager to do *something* about the population problem, but in the face of a negative, or at best unclear position on the part of high church authorities, is naturally reluctant to engage in direct programs. Research however is permissible, and several Catholic institutions are about to embark on programs which go beyond AUK type surveys and which actually include contraceptive advice as part of the research design.

On the other hand, research can be used to delay action. A highly placed adviser to the Jamaican government publicly accused our Jamaican research project of holding up action on the part of the government. It got them off the hook, he charged, by letting them say, "Let's wait until all the facts are in." Undoubtedly, many a Latin American bishop over the next decade will be delighted to turn the problem of population increase over to church scientists to investigate so that a difficult decision can be postponed. In my opinion, if the authorities are so ambivalent about action, the additional two or three years which such research might delay action is more than compensated for by the utility of the data provided—in other words, where commitment is weak it is especially important to have a structurally sound program.

Nevertheless, the timing of such studies, if they are to have more than academic interest, is vital. As an example, let me elaborate on the Jamaican project to which reference has already been made. In terms of many aspects of strategy this was a model project. Before the research began contact was made with high officials representing the Crown and the two political parties. It was decided that a local board should be officially created to give official sponsorship to the research, to facilitate the work of the investigators, to receive the final report, and to make recommendations based on this report. The Jamaica Population Research Foundation, chaired by a distinguished Jamaican physician, was composed of representatives from labor, industry, the clergy, the University, the professors, etc., and cut across political lines. In order to maintain interest, fairly frequent meetings were held to inform them of the progress of the research. It was felt that getting this group involved in the research would greatly improve the chances that some concrete action would emerge.

Secondly, every effort was made to produce a report rapidly which would be of practical utility. Only weeks after the last interviews were completed, several hundred copies of a simply written research report were distributed by the Jamaica Population Research Foundation. A staff member then wrote several newspaper articles summarizing the report. The report itself showed that the lower classes of Jamaica were interested in family planning and could be induced to practice it by means of a relatively modest program. Thus the conditions seemed absolutely ideal for implementation of the report. What happened? Absolutely nothing. Indeed, several years later when I returned to the island, I discovered that new key people in the relevant ministries had never heard of our study. What went wrong? I believe it was the timing. Given the delicate political balance, the degree of commitment to action in this area was insufficient on the part of the Jamaicans. The research was truly premature. The moral of this story is that research does not accomplish miracles in the real world: it accelerates, decelerates, or precipitates programs which would in time occur anyway.

Let me now describe two types of surveys which I believe will create major impacts in Latin America. The first is an organized international series of AUK surveys; the second, an as yet unorganized set of studies of induced abortions in Latin America.

A few years ago a series of conversations were held between myself and Carmen Miró, director of the U.N. Demographic Training and Research Center (CELADE) in Santiago, Chile. I had just completed a survey in Peru, and CELADE had just completed one in Chile. Neither of us had known of the other study. A third study was being initiated in Mexico, with little benefit of the experience of the other two. We decided the time was ripe to do a series of fertility surveys employing comparable samples, questionnaires, and design. CELADE personnel visited a number of countries and elicited sufficient interest to launch, in collaboration with the International Population Program at Cornell University, the following proposal:

AUK surveys would be carried out more or less simultaneously in the major city of an important group of countries. In each city about 2,000 women in the reproductive age group would be systematically sampled. Personal interviews would be conducted, employing a basic questionnaire devised by the CELADE and Cornell staffs. The plan required a sponsoring institution in each nation, and a full-time local survey director attached to that institution. In most instances CELADE graduates would be contacted. Each local institution was to have rights to analyze and publish its own analysis, but each was to supply a set of

IBM cards to CELADE. CELADE and Cornell shared responsibility for international comparisons.

The plan seemed to have a number of advantages: First, national research would be encouraged and facilitated, but without sacrificing international comparability; second, the provision of research funds and technical assistance to CELADE graduates would strengthen their position in the home institution and give them needed research experience; third, the participation of a U.N. organization, an American university, and other Latin American nations would make it much easier for any given country to sponsor such a delicate project, and might even make such a country concerned that it not be left out.

The response has been heartening. Seven countries are committed to the survey—Argentina, Brazil, Colombia, Costa Rica, Mexico, Panama, and Venezuela. (Peru and Chile were not included because similar studies had already been accomplished there.) The sponsoring institutions include universities, international organizations, national statistical agencies, and combinations of these. Funds were provided by the Population Council, and during the summer of 1963 a training seminar for the study directors was held in Santiago. At that time, U.N., Cornell, and CELADE personnel designed the questionnaire, instructed the group in sampling techniques, demonstrated interviewer training techniques, pretested the questionnaire, and had the seminar do hand tallies of the ensuing data. The interview includes a fertility history and questions relating to knowledge of and attitudes toward population growth, fertility, and contraception. Brazil, Panama, and Venezuela have already completed their field work and most of the others have initiated the field work. Of particular interest is the fact that two countries, on their own, sent observers to watch the field work in Panama. Eventually we expect to hold a seminar on analysis of the data and possibly to extend the survey to rural areas.

Judging by the success of those countries which have completed their field work and by the similarity of results in the earlier Peruvian and Chilean surveys, I expect the surveys to demonstrate motivation for small families combined with ignorance of the means for achieving a restricted family size. These surveys may alter substantially the thinking of Latin American elites concerning population problems and population control possibilities since they will reveal an absence of class differentiation in number of children desired and in attitude toward birth control, but marked class differentials in contraceptive practice and in family size.

A second type of study which will have major consequences for policy in Latin America refers to the epidemiology of induced abortion. Several years ago Chilean public health researchers became interested in the incidence of induced abortion in Chile. Attention was turned to this problem partly as a result of conflict between differing sectors of the National Health Service. Women with complications due to induced abortions began to flood both the "emergency hospitals" and the wards of the maternity services. Since both agencies were already overcrowded with other types of patients, each wished to push responsibility for the care of abortion cases on to the other. Precise information on the incidence of hospitalized abortion cases seemed indicated, and a subsequent study showed both a surprising incidence and a surprising increase in the incidence.

It was found that in recent years about 20 abortion complications were admitted for every 100 live births in hospitals and that between 1938 and 1960 the number of abortion cases had more than tripled.

After these results were reported to an international congress of social medicine in Chile in 1962 reactions were marked both on Chileans and foreigners. This tabooed subject had earlier gone unstudied and undiscussed. But if Chile could study the problem, why not other countries? Other countries soon began "discovering" similar data.

In Chile, the medical profession had largely been unconvinced of a population problem. Average population density was low and large areas of land were unexploited. In any event their task was to save life, not prevent it—let the economists worry about population and economic development. But this was different. Abortion complications were expensive and competing for overcrowded bed space and facilities. Interest in contraception multiplied—contraception would reduce abortion but not the birth rate—it was merely a substitute for abortion. While the rightists saw abortion as expensive, the leftists saw contraception as correcting class inequalities. Why should the upper classes have modern contraception and the lower classes abortion? A number of public hospitals quietly initiated contraceptive programs. When Ofelia Mendoza of International Planned Parenthood Federation's Western Hemisphere branch organized an open meeting on family planning for the Chilean Women's Medical Association in 1962, Santiago physicians were amazed to discover that not only they but their colleagues were actively interested in and often doing something about family planning services. A National Committee for the Protection of the Family was formed that was composed of the country's leading doctors of public health, obstetrics, and gynecology. At first announced as an official body of the National Health Service, it subsequently became an incorporated private organizaton, a major function of which is to set basic standards for research and co-ordinate the various research efforts on family planning under way in Chile.

Various kinds of research questions are being raised: (1) What is the incidence of induced abortion in the general population? University of Chile epidemiologists Armijo and Monreal have completed a systematic sample of Santiago women twenty to forty-four and found that a quarter of the 1,900 women had had an induced abortion.[3] A similar study is now under way in a provincial city, and a rural sample is also being planned. (2) To what extent and how rapidly can a contraceptive program reduce the abortion rate, and will the birth rate be affected? (3) Will a program utilizing intra-uterine devices have different consequences from those employing oral tablets or conventional contraceptives? Research projects employing before and after surveys are now in the planning stages at several Chilean institutions.

Chile is ahead of other Latin countries both in research and programs, and its experience will strongly influence other Latin nations. This does not mean, however, that replication of Chilean research, whether biomedical or social, will be unnecessary.

Among Latin American nations there is a strong sense, rightly or wrongly, of cultural and even biological uniqueness. Findings in country A will stimulate B to think about itself, but any research is likely to be undertaken in order to prove that B is different. This may not be scientifically justifiable, but for the reasons outlined at the beginning of this paper, it is probably a good idea.

[3] See Paper 13 above, "Epidemiology of Provoked Abortion in Santiago, Chile."

15

Discussion of Papers 11–14

LEO A. KAPRIO

CHAIRMAN KIMBALL: I think you will all agree with me that we have heard four very stimulating papers. We are fortunate in having an outstanding person to lead the discussion. I do not think he needs much of an introduction, but some of you may be interested in a little bit of his background. He did his medical work at Helsinki University; he got his Master of Public Health at Hopkins and his Doctor of Public Health at Harvard. He has held several responsible public health positions in Finland and has been associated in various capacities with the World Health Organization since 1956. At present he is director of the Division of Public Health Services for the World Health Organization at Geneva. Dr. Leo Kaprio.

KAPRIO: Thank you very much for your kind introduction. I am very happy to be here, especially today since we are to discuss a very interesting topic.

What is not clear from my career description is the fact that the problem we are now discussing is not unfamiliar to me. I was demobilized from the army in 1944 when we ended our war in Finland. Then one of my first tasks was to dig into the postwar abortion situation, which was quite serious. After listening to some of the anthropological and sociological discussions of the situation today I can realize that there were three factors that influenced our situation. There was a feminist movement which was led by the social democratic ladies. There was a bad medical problem, that is to say, extremely large numbers of illegal abortions and, since not many antibiotics were available at that time, these were really dangerous. Also, because the war had ended in defeat there was not much nationalistic feeling left in the country, and the increase in population was not very noticeable. In a relatively short time we were successful in developing marriage guidance clinics with the Maternal and Child Health services. With the help of Abraham Stone, we were able to open clinics, and we were also able to introduce liberal abortion legislation, which meant that women seeking abortions could directly approach official clinics and get advice regarding either abortion or other means of helping them in their difficulties. I myself was involved in the program, first in relation to voluntary organizations and later in my official capacity. We have moved into what I would call a Scandinavian situation where I do not think we have too many problems in this field now among the married part of the population. We still have, of course, problems in the unmarried part of the population, and questions related to the sex habits and balances among the youth and so on, but these topics are not pertinent to our present discussion.

I also was told that it would be good if there was an outsider to put the first question when we had the whole Western Hemisphere under discussion. After listening to the presentations I realized that there are problems both in North America and in Latin America, even if they are different from each other.

If I refer to my present position in the World Health Organization, you have to realize that, although we are in an intergovernmental agency, we have been criticized to the effect that we are not dealing with family planning questions and that our lack of action in this field reflects only the policies of the member governments who are guiding us. This includes the government in the United States. There is not much possibility for the Secretariat to move independently. However, there have been some movements in recent years. Dr. Stycos quite correctly mentioned that research is not controversial. In the field of research into human reproduction we have been able to co-operate with the U.S. government since 1963 to take some steps.

Regarding the papers, I think we are all very thankful for the very clear, interesting presentations. I would like to put some questions to each of the speakers.

I would have liked to hear a little bit more from Dr. Guttmacher about the abortion situation, especially illegal abortions in the United States. He mentioned uncontrolled fertility as a big problem, but how big is it really?

Then, Dr. Corsa was discussing the state problems. I felt there was a peculiar geographical distribution of the states that have a kind of official birth control program. Is there any reason why it is concentrated more in the southern states of the United States? Also, I was wondering how you feel about the training of doctors. On the educational side, is the medical profession well prepared to take this kind of responsibility when this type of program is involved?

Then, about Drs. Armijo's and Monreal's paper, I know many of us would like them to elaborate on the reliability of the information obtained from the social workers. I think they can do that easily. Secondly, can they tell us something of the extension of the studies to other parts of Chile, the rural areas.

Dr. Stycos' presentation was full of provocative comments in many directions. There is, I think, one point that I would like to confirm about what he said. About seventeen years ago Dr. Kinsey was lecturing to an audience here, and those of us in that group who had not very much to do with marriage guidance were quite shocked by the fact that the groups who go through longer formal education seem to be much more complicated in their approach to the sexual life than those entering, let me say, the manual labor force. So, I think that we are sometimes creating attitudes of complications among the intellectual groups. Some problems may not exist in the same form among the population groups at large. I think Dr. Stycos pointed out that there may be quite clear motivations if the proper means in relation to the motivation are provided for larger population groups.

CHAIRMAN KIMBALL: I think it would be appropriate to ask the speakers first to reply to Dr. Kaprio's comments and then we will open the floor for discussion from the other participants. I will call first on Dr. Guttmacher.

GUTTMACHER: First of all, we know so little about the extent of illegal abortion in North America. We do have estimates, of course, that in the United States, according to the Kinsey figures, there is one illegal abortion for every five pregnancies, which, since we have about 4.25 million children born yearly, would give us a figure somewhere in the area of a million illegal abortions per year.

This is simply a guess. No one really knows whether this is an accurate figure or not, but those of us who have practiced obstetrics and gynecology feel that it may be an underestimation rather than an overestimation, because we are constantly approached for advice on the problem. We do know something about legal abortion in America, and we are ashamed to say that the rate is approximately 2 per 1,000 births. So we have 1 legal abortion in 500 pregnancies in America. This is a scandalously low rate. It is low because obviously there are innumerable women who should be aborted but cannot be aborted legally in this country.

Currently, I am very much concerned by the fact that I was called up by a woman who was raped by two men. The men were apprehended. They were identified by fourteen women who had apparently also been raped. My woman became pregnant. She had called up about half a dozen physicians in New York to have an illegal abortion done and, of course, they had refused her. So she called me up and I was sufficiently concerned to take it up with my former hospital, Mount Sinai. I was not given permission to do the illegal abortion. I had to send her to an illegal abortionist and, of course, this is a common pattern. In our country we are so stubborn and conservative that we will not even carry out abortion when there is a crying need. And when American medicine boasts that we have one of the lowest abortion rates in the world, it is boasting about a rate which is absolutely inhuman and which in no sense carries out what has to be done.

I am a little more liberal about this. I send some women to a very good abortionist in Japan, where it is quite legal; if the women are less than twelve weeks' pregnant, he does a very fine job. I am very grateful to my Japanese colleague for giving me this help. But when people cannot afford to go to Japan, then I have to confront them with the indignity of having an illegal abortion done in America.

In America, the quality of illegal abortions is in proportion to what the patient can afford to pay. According to the Kinsey figures, about 70 per cent of our abortions are done by physicians. Some of my best friends were abortionists or are abortionists. I am always amazed to pick up *The New York Times* and discover that a member of my staff, the chief of service of one of the large hospitals in New York, was indicted for abortion, not only for one abortion but for sixteen abortions. These are members of the American College of Obstetrics and Gynecology. These are fellows who parade around just like the rest of us as good doctors, but men of this stature do perform abortions.

Now, people who can get to these men are very lucky because they come away whole and sound. The difficulties, of course, are that not everybody can afford them and secondly, that many people are too unsophisticated to know doctors to go to to have an abortion. In short, if you can afford a good abortionist, you can get away with it.

However, not everybody gets away with it because 48 per cent of the puerperal deaths in New York City in 1953–62 were due to illegal abortion. I dare say it's a larger figure than this, but these are the ones that the coroner's office reported. If you study this group by skin color and race, you find that risk of death from abortion was nine times greater among nonwhites than whites (74.9 abortion deaths among nonwhites per 100,000 live births compared to 8.4 among whites). The risk to the Puerto Rican is intermediate (46.7 per 100,000 live births). This does not mean that Negroes provoke abortion nine times as frequently as do the whites. It is likely that the true racial incidence figures are reversed. It means that the white woman has the sophistication and the means to buy a safe abortion, while the Negro must abort herself or be aborted by some unsafe paramedical abortionist. I think that we should be scandalized by the abortion situation in North America. I know little about Latin America except what the speakers have told us, but I certainly do not feel complacent about the situation here.

CHAIRMAN KIMBALL: Thank you very much, Dr. Guttmacher. I will call on Dr. Corsa next.

CORSA: Before I try to answer Dr. Kaprio's questions I would like to add a supporting postscript to Dr. Guttmacher's word about abortions. The situation in California is quite similar to the figures he gave for New York City. The 48 per cent there is on the order of 35 per cent in California. A similar differential in skin color also exists. As I mentioned briefly in my presentation, a number of groups in California during the last session of the Legislature introduced legislation to liberalize the abortion laws of California. The intent was to provide automatic permission for abortion in cases of rape, to liberalize the present very restrictive law to permit an abortion in case of any hazard to the physical or mental health of the mother or infant and to leave the decision with regard to whether there is such a problem in the hands of a small, qualified board in each qualified hospital.

This law was controversial. It was not passed, but in the interim period since the session of the Legislature last year it has received considerably increased support, and I think that it has a fighting chance in the 1965 Legislature in California. We hope so.

As to the question of the knowledge of the medical profession in the United States with regard to contraceptive technology, I would say that, by and large, it is quite adequate. With regard to traditional methods and the pill, there is a limited amount of instruction in medical schools at the present time. There is a move afoot to improve this, but contraception is widely practiced in the United States, and one of the principal sources of advice is the private physician.

There will, of course, be special problems in not keeping practicing physicians abreast of the more rapid changes in contraceptive technology as they occur. The knowledge of physicians about population growth and its problems is quite another story, and it is an area where medical schools and postgraduate education of physicians can stand considerable improvement in the United States as well as elsewhere.

The knowledge of the public health nurses or the professional people, in our local health departments, who deal with the special problems of the low economic group in this regard is not quite as good. I think that we have to give considerable help, so that many of them can move into a new program.

With regard to the geographic distribution of family planning services in state and local governmental agencies in the United States which Dr. Guttmacher and I mentioned earlier, it is, of course, limited to the southeastern United States, where there is a heavy concentration of poverty among the Negroes. The increase in activity in the United States in the last few years, I think, is probably related to this fact in the few areas where it is moving. Actually, there is considerable activity in twenty other states. In most instances, the principal source of active citizen support is from Dr. Guttmacher's organization and its local affiliates and state or local health officers with enough guts to take up what has been, up to the present time, a very controversial issue.

CHAIRMAN KIMBALL: Thank you. Dr. Armijo?

ARMIJO: I have been asked several times how reliable our data is. From the very beginning, when we started the study, some of my friends would say that we were crazy to think that we could knock on the door and then say, "Good morning, madam, how many abortions have you had?" and expect to obtain reliable answers.

But the reliability of our data is related to several aspects—the sample itself, reliability of our social workers, and the reliability of the women who furnished the information. Regarding the sample, we tested our distribution characteristics against a 1 per cent subsample of the census, and with the exception of a few minor deviations, our sample corresponded fairly well to the distribution characteristics in the universe as a whole.

The reasons for using social workers and the methods of training and of supervising them have been described in our paper.

KAPRIO: What about the rural areas? The expansion of your studies?

ARMIJO: I want to say that the findings of this study are applicable only to Santiago. Santiago is our capital city. Chile is a country with a population of 8 million people and 2.5 million are concentrated in

Santiago. It is said that Santiago is Chile and Chile is Santiago, but we feel that we are very much interested in trying to find out what happens with abortions outside Santiago. Thanks to the generous contribution of the Population Council we have been able to extend our study to an industrial city in the south. So far, we have already interviewed about 700 women, and the results and findings will be coming out in the near future. Our next step will be to study a large mining area in the north.

We are planning also a joint study with the Latin American Demographic Center of the rural areas of Chile, but it will take some more time before we learn anything from these new studies.

CHAIRMAN KIMBALL: Thank you. I think at this point we can open the floor for discussion.

KIRK: I want to ask Dr. Corsa what his evidence is for the statement that physicians are the principal source of information on contraception in the United States. The surveys of the general population show that the condom is the leading form of contraception in the United States and that the methods prescribed by physicians are in the minority in use. I wonder if you would like to speak on that.

CORSA: No, I don't. You are correct.

HEER: I have a question for Dr. Guttmacher. Has the Executive Committee of the Planned Parenthood Federation of America considered the possibility that the Federation might take a stand in favor of liberalizing federal and state laws concerning abortion and, if so, what has been the tenor of the discussion?

GUTTMACHER: I have not had the fortitude to even present this to them. We wanted them to accept sterilization in our program. We have two separate units in the United States. One is called Planned Parenthood and the other is called Human Betterment. The former supports temporary contraception and the latter seeks permanent contraception. I think I would have a tough time in getting them to take a stand on a liberalization of abortion laws.

It is interesting that in England they have the Abortion Reform Association, of which Lord Horder at one time was the chairman and now Williams is. They are not making much progress to be sure, but they have some excellent names, and they are organized. In the United States we have a few little organizations in California, but no well-organized effort for the nation as a whole. It is rather striking that we have not organized ourselves into a group really to attempt to beat down the opposition. It is going to take a long time.

CHAIRMAN KIMBALL: Dr. Balfour?

BALFOUR: I would like to ask Dr. Armijo if the results of the abortion study in Santiago produce any evidence or any judgments concerning the harmfulness or the harmlessness of one or more abortions? I realize it is hard to collect this kind of information, but we hear a great deal about the harmfulness of abortions and yet there is very little evidence on this point.

ARMIJO: We are still tabulating the data, and I am afraid that I would not be able to answer that specific question. Of the women interviewed, we found that one woman had admitted to thirty-five provoked abortions, but we have not yet tabulated our data in order to determine the harmfulness or the harmlessness of abortions.

PEASE: I would like to ask Dr. Stycos if he would be willing to elaborate on his comment on the difference between the attitude of the Latin Americans as compared to the North American physicians on this problem?

STYCOS: No, sir.

PEASE: Thank you.

CHAIRMAN KIMBALL: Dr. Sheps?

SHEPS: I would like to ask Dr. Armijo a number of questions to which he perhaps does not yet have the answers, but I would like to suggest that he might be interested in further analysis.

One is that the number of abortions per woman or the number of instances of abortion by age is obviously related to the number of pregnancies and that an analysis in which the number of pregnancies rather than the women themselves is considered might shed some added light.

Secondly, I wondered whether the age incidence in Table 2, which is certainly affected in part by the frequency in pregnancies and in which the peak of abortions is in the age group twenty-five to twenty-nine, probably is related to the fact that that is the peak age for pregnancies in this group. Also, since a woman who is twenty-five cannot tell you anything about abortions after the age twenty-five, whereas a woman who is forty can tell you about her abortions for her whole reproductive history, it seems to me that the age distribution of the women in the sample might be very important in the results in Table 2.

Then, I think that it is quite possible that some unknown proportion of the abortions that were said to be spontaneous might actually have been induced. If an analysis is done on those abortions as well as the ones that are induced and if you can find differences in the age distribution, class differentials, and so on, I think that it might also be of interest.

Finally, I wondered about some correlations. For example, what is the relationship between the use of contraception and the incidence of abortion?

CHAIRMAN KIMBALL: Dr. Armijo, do you care to comment on one or more of these questions?

ARMIJO: The first question dealt with the relation of abortions to pregnancies. We found for the decade 1952–61 the ratio of all abortions to 100 live births was 40.1 as is shown in Table 3; for provoked abortions it was 23.3. This is a retrospective analysis. Now, these data were tested against what we found for the particular year 1961, which was the year prior to the interview, and the corresponding ratios found for that particular year were 45.6 and 22.6. Thus these data agree with each other to a great extent.

The retrospective analysis was based on the assumption that each woman had theoretically been observed since the age fifteen. Each woman was followed up backward. This retrospective analysis gave us a chance to estimate the rates or incidences which are shown in Table 2. Again, I say that this analysis was tested against the figures found for the year 1961, the year prior to the survey, because we felt that recent abortions might be kept in mind more easily than abortions occurring in the past. We found that the highest attack rate in 1961 was in the twenty-five to twenty-nine year age group, with an attack rate of 12.8 per 100 women. This was the attack rate for all abortions.

We are not sure whether a good proportion of provoked abortions has been reported as "spontaneous." That is why throughout the whole study we find the figures relating to total abortions and induced abortions. We feel pretty sure that the error must work in the direction of underreporting as far as provoked abortions are concerned. In other words, the real situation must be worse than that shown in our figures.

As to the relationship between the use of contraceptives and abortion rates, we wanted to find that out, but since this was a house-to-house inquiry and since we had to work out a kind of retrospective analysis, we could not find any reliable information about that particular aspect because it would have had to be worked out on the basis of a follow-up study.

SHEPS: I meant a cross-tabulation for women who said that they did use or had used contraceptives at some times.

ARMIJO: Yes, but the trouble was that this was the distribution of women using some sort of contraception at the moment when interviewed; we would have to break these figures down according to the number of years of exposure, the number of years of using contraceptives, and so on and so forth in order to do such an analysis.

POLGAR: I would like to make a suggestion. As a number of you probably know, at one of the regional meetings of the American Assembly, which has been referred to previously in our discussions here, a proposal was put forward to make 1970 International Population Study Year, and I think that there is a lot of merit to this proposal. I do not know what its fate is going to be.

Now, I think that Dr. Armijo's excellent study as well as a number of other remarks made here make the subject of induced abortions a very logical item of proposed investigation that might be prepared for the eventuality that such an international population study will take place in 1970.

Yesterday, Dr. Hill also made some suggestions regarding the studies in the age of marriage and the factors that affect that, and I think that might very well be another topic to be included.

MENDOZA: I would like to ask a question of Dr. Guttmacher. I have heard practically all the risks of illegal abortion, but I have not heard one word about the risks of therapeutic abortion.

GUTTMACHER: About therapeutic abortions, as far as death is concerned, I cannot give you any U.S. figures, though I guess they could be obtained, but since we only do about 9,000 legal abortions a year in the United States, any figure I would give would be relatively unimportant.

We have some very good figures from Hungary and Czechoslovakia. They give us the risk figure per 100,000 legal abortions. These abortions are all done in the hospital, and they are almost all done on pregnancies of less than twelve weeks' duration. Only 1 per cent of the pregnancies are more than twelve weeks, but there must be a serious organic health reason to do an abortion beyond twelve weeks in Hungary and Czechoslovakia.

In one country you have a risk figure of 6 deaths per 100,000 and in the other you have 3.5 per 100,000. If you put these together, it gives you a risk figure of 5 deaths per 100,000 legal abortions in Hungary and Czechoslovakia.

Now, these are not only social abortions but also abortions necessitated by serious organic diseases, such as heart disease or some other organic lesion, and most of the deaths fall within this latter category. In the same areas you have a maternal mortality of about 49 per 100,000 live births, so that if you will accept this over-all figure of 5 for these two countries and also the figure of 49 for maternal mortality, then, theoretically, even including women who are seriously ill, the danger from a therapeutic abortion performed after less than twelve weeks of pregnancy in a hospital in these two countries is one-tenth the danger of having a live birth. That is the best figure I can give you. I do not know of anything better.

CORSA: Can we hear from Dr. Muramatsu on this?

MURAMATSU: About five or six years ago a group of obstetrician-gynecologists in Japan conducted a similar study to this, and I can tell you that our figure came out to be 7 or 8 deaths per 100,000 abortions. The abortions were performed mostly in the private doctor's office.

GUTTMACHER: I think that is a remarkable figure. Seven or eight deaths per 100,000 abortions performed in the doctor's office is to me a more impressive figure than that of 5 deaths for abortions done in hospitals. Are these also pregnancies of twelve weeks or less?

MURAMATSU: Yes, I say nearly 95 per cent of all these cases studied were performed before the end of the third lunar month.

YANG: I would like to ask Dr. Armijo if the majority of induced abortion cases he studied was performed by midwives. I want to know whether this reflects the cost of the abortion or whether Chilean hospitals are closed to those women who want to have abortions. Or are these women living in remote places where only midwives are available? Why is the majority performed by midwives? Also, I want to know what kind of method is used.

ARMIJO: To start with, abortion is illegal in Chile. Regulations are strict, and the punishment in proven cases is quite severe for the woman and for the one who caused the abortion. That is one of the reasons why women have to seek somebody who is willing to perform abortions behind the door. A minority of them go to a doctor because only a few doctors are ready to do abortions; furthermore, few women can afford to pay for a doctor.

Graduate midwives in Chile are trained on a European pattern. They are high school graduates, and they go into the university for a three-year course. Some of these midwives would be ready to help a woman and the majority of the abortions is done by them. As a matter of fact, these abortions are done by the midwives on the side to supplement their incomes.

You asked how much they charge. That depends on the midwife and on the woman, but I would say they would charge roughly about $30. These midwives are those who charge the lowest prices and, for the most part, do a pretty good job. The mortality rate of the abortions admitted to hospitals which have a heavy concentration of the most severe cases of incomplete abortions is 5 per 1,000. Most of the abortions admitted into hospitals are those done by amateur midwives.

The self-induced abortion is quite a problem. Eleven per cent of our abortions were self-induced by the woman herself, and these, of course, are very risky.

The most favorite method of abortion was the insertion of a rubber tube into the cervix. About 50 per cent used different rubber tubes in the cervix.

STYCOS: I would like to comment. You understand we are in the realm of spiritual values here, which are difficult to define. *Machismo* is the term that covers a kind of supposed complex for proving one's virility by means of certain behavioral patterns, in particular in having a large number of children. That is the term we are concerned with. When I spoke of an intellectual pattern in Latin America among the upper classes, I was speaking of a kind of ideological *machismo*, that is, the feeling on the part of the intellectual classes that to reduce or to slow down the rate of population growth or the fertility of a nation is a kind of cultural castration and that this, in a sense, offends those who feel that the nation or the people as a good thing is a thing that must grow. This definition holds for anything we want.

You see, the first book I referred to [Hatt, *Backgrounds of Human Fertility in Puerto Rico*] is the one that laid out the hypothesis that there might be this drive for manifesting one's virility among males which kept males continuing to have a large number of children. This was based on psychiatric type interviews and relatively few cases. When we attempted to test this on a larger and more representative sample, we found that we could observe very little relation between any indices we had of *machismo* and actual behavior or really even attitude on the part of males. What we did find, however, which is very interesting and again is in the ideological realm, is that wives overestimated, as did the investigators, the importance of this particular motivation in men, at least as reported by the men themselves when they were asked directly, and men overestimated the importance of complexes such as modesty in their wives as checked against their wives' own statements.

So, you have sexual stereotypes here that were long established, and because of the relative absence of communication on these topics, each sex is attributing to the other a complex which is more important in their minds than its effect on actual behavior.

ARMIJO: I want to add a little comment as a Latin American. In our country, in spite of the fact that we have removed much of this *machismo* feeling, you may find an example illustrating to what extent the *machismo* is an attitude reflected in many provisions in our criminal code. It was made by men in the past century, and there are two different definitions of adultery, one for the woman and the other for the man. The definition for the woman is something like this. A married woman commits adultery when she has sexual intercourse with a man who is not her husband, and that is all. The definition for the man is different. A married man commits adultery when he has sexual intercourse with a woman who is not his wife inside the home or outside the home with scandal.

HILL: I apologize for posing a question that takes you away from this, but I would like to know what documentation Dr. Corsa might bring to bear on his assertion that medical schools and physicians in this country have had adequate training to provide contraceptive advice. What proportion of schools do offer such training? What proportion of physicians did not get such training because they took their training before it was offered and did come back for refresher training? I am asking this from the standpoint of the person trying to make a referral, say, in a premarital counseling situation. Do we have a documentation?

CORSA: No, we don't. Dr. Eliot's committee is about to document the situation with regard to teaching of medical students at the present time. I do not know of any documentation. They are just touching the group at different points, and obviously we have touched different groups at different points. This is something that we perhaps need to document further.

PART III

TRAINING PROGRAMS

16

The Social Scientist's Contribution to Action and Training Programs

DUDLEY KIRK

Population programs draw on many skills. The field of family planning is a new, an interstitial, and at this stage an amorphous discipline. The range of talents that may contribute is suggested by a partial list of subjects from which the Ford Foundation has drawn experts to advise and to assist the government of India in the implementation of its family planning program.

Biomedical Sciences	*Health Sciences*	*Social Sciences*
Embryology	Biostatistics	Demography
Endocrinology	Epidemiology	Economics
Immunology	Health administra-	Rural sociology
Obstetrics and Gyne-	tion	Social anthropology
cology	Health education	
Reproductive physi-	Maternal-child health	Sociology
ology		

In addition to the above, experts were brought to assist in special technical fields such as audio-visual communication and contraceptive manufacture, especially of rubber products.

Whatever the need for each of the specific fields mentioned above, it is clear that a very wide spectrum is called for. Population programs and the study of family planning do not fit readily into the fixed categories of our academic programs. In what follows I will be referring to one segment of the spectrum, Dr. Segal to another. But it

185

must be clear that there are no sharp dividing lines between the contributions of the social sciences and the health sciences, for example, or between the health sciences and the biomedical sciences, nor should there be.

For convenience I shall refer to contributions of social scientists under three headings: (1) Measurement and Definition of the Population Problem, (2) Survey Research and Action Experiment, and (3) Training.

Measurement and Definition of the Population Problem

I will not dwell long on this rather obvious contribution of social scientists and especially of the demographers. It has been the business of demographers to measure rates of population growth and to determine the factors affecting this growth. Demographers have done much to measure and define the population problem in the areas where it is most acute and with which we are here primarily concerned—the underdeveloped world. In most of this world economic underdevelopment is matched by statistical underdevelopment.

In recent years there has been a rapid development in this country of scientific skills to make the most of poor data in getting basic demographic measurements and projections. There is the new use of stable population analysis, of stochastic models, of the new computers, and so on. In these endeavors the demographers have had a close alliance with the biostatisticians, though the latter have generally focused more specifically on the measurement of mortality and causes of death. Using the available official statistics as corrected, evaluated, and supplemented, demographers have measured the population problem.

In the underdeveloped countries themselves demographers and social statisticians trained locally, in regional centers and in the advanced countries, are doing much to improve the data and to improve the measuring of trends in birth rates, death rates, and population growth.

Economists and sociologists, in partnership with demographers and using the basic data provided by the latter, have related population growth to problems of economic and social development. The accelerating rate of population growth and its effects as a handicap on economic and social development have been treated in numerous popular, semipopular, and technical works. Again it is not necessary to elaborate. Social scientists have done much to establish the facts and thereby the basis for intelligent awareness of the population problem and of the need for action.[1]

Survey Research and Action Experiment

The demographer as such is usually dealing with data for the population of countries as a whole, in macrocosm. But family planning is an intimate matter involving the actions of individual couples in microcosm. The social scientist has taken the lead in going into the field to find out what the typical couple thinks, knows, and does about family planning.

The number of such field studies is growing even more rapidly than the populations they are studying. I have made an informal count of some thirty such studies in the underdeveloped areas that can make some claim to scientific design and execution. These have been or are now being conducted in twenty countries of Asia, Africa, and Latin America. Some of these studies have been described at other sessions of this Conference. A majority were initiated by and are being directed by social scientists and especially sociologists-demographers. Others are being directed by public health and medical people: health educators, obstetrician-gynecologists, specialists in maternal-child health, epidemiologists, etc. In more recent studies, especially those having an action component, there has developed a pattern of team participation involving social scientists, health scientists, and medical personnel.

Of the studies to which I have referred about half are also action experiments introducing family planning. It is interesting that here the roles of the health sciences and of the social sciences tend to be reversed. The majority of the action experiments are under the direction of men drawn from public health or medicine. Measurement and evaluation is generally provided, if at all, by social scientists; the operational component is characteristically provided by physicians and by health educators and administrators.

The great majority of both the surveys and the action experiments has been undertaken in recent years, and relatively little of the results

---

[1] A convenient summary of the various agencies working in the field and the most important literature is to be found in "Focus on World Population," *Intercom*, Vol. 6, No. 1 (January–February, 1964), published by the Foreign Policy Associaton, New York.

of these studies have yet become available in print. Potentially these contain one of the most extensive collections of comparable cross-cultural studies available on any subject.[2]

What are the contributions of such studies to action programs? First, *Knowledge:* They have the very basic and important scientific function of ascertaining the facts. What are the attitudes of the general population toward the idea of family planning? Does a substantial part of the adult population wish to restrict the size of their families? What do they already know about methods of family planning and where did they get their information? To what extent do they actually practice family planning and by what methods? Such information is obviously of importance in the planning of an effective national action program.

Second, *"Market" research:* Such studies serve the function of determining the groups in the population that are now more or less ready for family planning. This is of obvious importance in determining the "targets" for any action program.

Third, *Testing:* The action experiments are pilot projects for testing the acceptability and the effectiveness of different methods of family planning, the efficiency of different educational methods, and the feasibility of varying types of administrative organization.

Fourth, *Evaluation:* Such studies offer at least the possibility of program evaluation. Up to the present they have generally been concerned with relatively small populations; only a few such studies, for example in Turkey and in Japan, have covered a national sample. Potentially, however, the survey approach offers an opportunity for obtaining baseline information and periodic check of the effectiveness of a national program. This may be particularly necessary where the national administration is weak and where there is very defective reporting of vital events, etc., as is characteristic of underdeveloped areas.

Quite as important as the above are two indirect functions of survey research and action experiment. In most countries there is a major gap

[2] The plans and results of a number of such studies are given in Clyde V. Kiser (ed.), *Research in Family Planning* (Princeton: Princeton University Press, 1962) and in Ronald Freedman, "The Sociology of Human Fertility: A Trend Report and Bibliography," *Current Sociology,* Vol. X/XI, No. 2 (1961–62), published by UNESCO. Up-to-date summaries of ongoing studies are given in *Studies in Family Planning,* Nos. 1–4 (July, 1963–August, 1964), published by the Population Council. The majority of the studies were in one way or another financed or sponsored by the Population Council.

of understanding between the political leadership and the masses. In the field of family planning this is likely to take the form of a feeling by the governing elite that the lower classes are irresponsible, not interested in undertaking family planning, and unable to carry out effective family planning even if interested. In every country the individuals composing the governing groups are aware of methods of family planning and themselves generally practice it; at the same time they assume that the general public is uninterested. Most field studies have shown this to be incorrect—the average person is concerned about family size and in all cases a substantial number of couples is interested in receiving information and appropriate supplies. Thus the studies may have important effects in educating the policy makers.

A second indirect value of these studies is that they may be an uncontroversial way of initiating activity. Governments that are reluctant openly to adopt a national family planning policy may be quite ready to have the subject studied and to have experimental projects. The projects themselves in turn create interests and better knowledge of the local situations and in this way may contribute to the crystallization of national policy.

It would be tempting to summarize the findings of the surveys and action studies, which are surprisingly uniform. These are a few of many possible generalizations:

1. The studies demonstrate the possibility of getting reliable information on so intimate a subject as family planning in almost every culture. Everywhere it is said, "You can't do it here." But you can. Even rural, illiterate, traditional-minded persons give surprisingly complete and ready answers to inquiries in this field, so long as the interviewer is defined as a professional outsider. An interesting point is that men prove generally to be somewhat more reliable informants on sexual practices, use of contraception, etc., than women.

2. In every country there is at least a substantial minority who wants smaller families, is interested in obtaining information on family planning, and is willing to try it. As might be expected, the more "advanced" segments of each national population are more favorably disposed than the illiterate, the poverty-stricken, and the traditional-minded. This is especially true with reference to the actual practice of family planning. Thus, there is a range in attitudes toward family planning from "strong consensus in all strata of the society" in Taiwan down to an expression of favorable attitudes by 30 per cent or so of the eligible couples as found in Pakistan studies. Obviously the determi-

nation of "eligible" couples is complicated by such factors as age, number of living children (especially sons), present pregnancy, lactation. But it may be stated as a generalization that in all of the societies studied the majority of parents with three or four living children do not want more. It is interesting that men and women commonly show about the same percentage of favorable attitudes toward family planning, though presumably men are less strongly motivated than women in the direction of actual practice of family planning. At any given time there is a substantial "market" for family planning in every country studied.

3. Such motivation is characteristically combined with ignorance of sexual physiology and especially of appropriate methods of family planning. The problem confronting a nation introducing a population control program is more likely to be that of communication, i.e., the supply of information and services, than it is of motivation. In every country there is a very large need that has not as yet been met. It is not necessary to devote much effort toward persuasion—the need already exists. In any case there is a strong suggestion that the "satisfied user" is the best vehicle of persuasion.

4. Methods *do* make a difference. Earlier action experiments that ignored the traditional methods of contraception, such as the condom and the rhythm method, have generally failed. Thus, the diaphragm, which was almost universally prescribed by American physicians a few years ago, has not fared well in the underdeveloped areas, nor has the foam tablet. The surveys show that in Asia, as in Europe, the male methods had been most successful until the innovation of the very new methods. There is one very important exception: the practice of coitus interruptus has not been generally adopted outside European culture where historically it received very wide, almost universal acceptance. The situation is now changed by two new methods used by women, the oral contraceptive and the intra-uterine device. These are revolutionizing the programs for introducing family planning in underdeveloped areas. The fact that they may be adopted and used independently of the sex act is of crucial importance in their acceptance. But new methods create new problems. The chief barrier to the wider acceptance of the oral pill is its cost; acceptance of the intra-uterine device is hindered by the fact that it must be inserted by a physician under present recommended usage. This creates a major problem in countries where medical services, and especially the number of women physicians, is quite inadequate to cope.

5. Elaborate, indirect approaches in introducing family planning seem to be no more effective, and certainly less efficient, than direct and forthright approaches. There is no indication that there is a need to search for ways of providing deep psychological motivation and elaborate build-up before introducing the family planning program. It may well be that it is not necessary to conceal the family planning program within a general health program, though this procedure may be desirable for purely administrative reasons. House-to-house and face-to-face approaches requiring a large investment of personnel have not proven conspicuously more successful than broadcast and quite simple approaches. This conflicts with sociological and communication theories but nevertheless seems to accord with the empirical experience in the countries studied.

There has been much talk about the need for expert help from the communications experts—to meet the needs for communication and motivation in carrying forward family planning programs. On this subject there have been good controlled experiments by Hill, Stycos, and Back in Puerto Rico, by Stycos and Back in Jamaica, and more recently by Freedman and Berelson in Taiwan.[3] These studies test the relative effectiveness of home visits, mailings, meetings, etc. The results have been rather anomalous, and quite different results have been achieved depending on the birth control methods offered in the experiments. Furthermore the "hard sell," using all methods of communication, has never been really tried, though an experiment along this line is being conducted in Korea. Much remains to be done; if there is one proper conclusion it is that at the moment the problem is less that of motivation than of communication. Everywhere there is a reservoir of potential users already motivated if ways can be found to inform them and to make available suitable methods.

Finally, I should mention another contribution that social scientists make along with others, especially those from health sciences: advisory missions and technical assistance to governments. References already have been made above to the many skills which have been drawn on to contribute to the program in India. Somewhat similar contributions on a smaller scale have been made in Pakistan, and in various ways social

[3] R. Hill, J. M. Stycos, and K. W. Back, *The Family and Population Control* (Chapel Hill, North Carolina Press, 1959). J. M. Stycos, and K. W. Back, *Prospects for Fertility Reduction: The Jamaica Family Life Project* (New York, Conservation Foundation, 1957). B. Berelson, and R. Freedman, "A Study in Fertility Control," *Scientific American* (May, 1964), pp 3–11.

scientists have participated in missions requested by the governments of Korea, Turkey, Tunisia, and Thailand.[4]

Training

In the last few years the study of population has been commonly regarded as falling within the academic discipline and administration of departments of sociology. As cause or consequence, the greatest development in the study of population, both theoretical and applied, has occurred in a few of the major centers within departments of sociology. Among these one may mention Brown, California, Chicago, Michigan, Pennsylvania, Princeton, and Wisconsin. The departments of sociology (and economics) in these institutions, rather more than the schools of public health, have taken the initiative in population study and training.

How many have been trained? In the last few years the study of population has been regarded as a highly specialized subject, and there have not been a great many American students trained in the field. Happily this situation is changing; a growing number of Americans are doing graduate work in demography and such training is increasingly being given in departments other than sociology, e.g., economics and public health. This development has been promoted by growing interest in population problems and in social and economic development. Study by Americans has been increasingly financed by such agencies as the National Institutes of Health.

Although the situation in the United States is not an optimal one, advanced academic training in population is still largely limited to the United States and to England and France. Grant-giving agencies have attempted to meet this situation in two ways: by bringing students to these countries for advanced training and by contributing to new local and regional centers in the underdeveloped areas. In the last ten years the Population Council has given demographic fellowships to some 200 persons for advanced graduate study in population, three-fourths of these being students from the underdeveloped areas, most of whom studied in the United States. The Council's objective has been to assist in training a small nucleus of qualified persons in each major country, people who can speak with authority and literally in the language and

[4] Summaries of the mission reports for Korea, Turkey, and Tunisia are given in *Studies in Family Planning*, No. 2 (December, 1963), pp. 1–6.

within the value context of the country concerned; only a handful, far too few, of these were trained in schools of public health.[5]

More recently the Council has established a fellowship program in family planning administration. Each year several fellows in this program are being trained at Hopkins and at other schools of public health.

To supplement training in advanced countries, the United Nations, with support from the Population Council and the Ford Foundation, has established three regional centers for training and research on population: (1) the Centro Latinamericano de Demografia in Santiago, Chile; (2) the Demographic Training and Research Centre for Asia and the Far East in Bombay; and (3) the Demographing Training and Research Centre for North Africa in Cairo. It would be unfair to attribute the establishment of these centers to any one group of disciplines. They have been created by the teamwork of persons from several disciplines within the social and health sciences. As a part of these teams social scientists have made a very important contribution to their establishment and to their activities. These centers have become major foci for regional training in population, for research, and for the expression of intelligent interest in regional population problems. Being under the United Nations' auspices they have not moved so far toward action programs as might otherwise have been the case. In general, they reflect the conservative consensus in the region where they exist. Thus, the Asian center has been more action-oriented than the Latin American center, though the latter has done much to promote work of relevance to family planning in that region.

Conclusion

I think it would be fair to say that social scientists have taken the primary initiative in study and research relevant to family planning programs. Put another way, the social scientists have dealt with the more scientific aspects in laying the factual and experimental groundwork for policy, rather than in carrying it out. Partly due to the findings of social scientists, the world climate of opinion in relation to family planning and government intervention is changing very rapidly. As we know a number of countries has adopted official family planning

[5] A listing of Population Council Fellows up to the date of publication is given in the Population Council *Newsletter*, No. 4 (Winter, 1962–63).

programs and a larger circle of countries has adopted experimentation in this area under government auspices. So long as family planning was in the stage of the private "birth control movement" it was not regarded as a health problem either by public health administrators or by schools of public health. But now action programs in introducing family planning are increasingly being regarded as within the purview of public health. Governments are turning more and more to the schools of public health for help. We social scientists who are interested in this problem are delighted to see this development and look forward to a growing partnership with the schools of public health in this very challenging enterprise.

17

Current Research on Methods as Related to the Training of Professional Workers

SHELDON J. SEGAL

In these days of ultraspecialization in science, new subspecialties are proclaimed almost as fast as identifying names can be coined. Usually, the new discipline first asserts itself by modestly requesting a special session or a half-day symposium at the annual meeting of the parent society. Next it is decided that the subject is so highly specialized that the pioneers should meet independently to exchange ideas. The idea most acceptable to all, it develops, is the creation of a new society. The charter members take this responsibility reluctantly after a full airing of the deplorable tendency toward subspecialization in science, but at the same time they appoint a committee to explore the feasibility of publishing a new journal.

Against this general pattern, it is unusual to witness the emergence of a scientific specialty based on inclusiveness rather than exclusiveness. From what has preceded in this Conference, I think it is apparent that the efforts in developing programs of voluntary fertility regulation have created exactly this—a discipline based on a coalescence of information from a broad spectrum of natural and social sciences.

With respect to the biomedical sciences, it is generally understood that the major contribution expected is the development of new, improved, simplified methodology for fertility regulation. This is, in fact, only one of several contributions of the biomedical sciences in the general program toward developing family planning methodology. There are, I believe, four major categories of participation of biomedical scientists. First, as already mentioned, is the important contribution through research toward development of new birth control methods. This is achieved by basic research on the physiology of human reproduction and by applied research in testing possible new contraceptive methods.

Second, biomedical scientists should take the responsibility of advising governmental policy makers in decisions requiring a background of technical knowledge. Only if indigenous scientists are up to a high level of competence in a given country can the policy makers call upon them for this important function.

Third, biomedical scientists can assist by informing the medical community of new developments and new methods of fertility control. This roll is important in order to minimize the time lag that may occur in the adoption of new methods of contraception. This period of delay can be greatly reduced if the medical community is oriented rather quickly in the history of a new means of contraception.

Finally, Biomedical Sciences should provide technical advice for the development of illustrative material about the reproductive process for the education of operational level family planning workers and for the public, a function that has become apparent as family planning programs move ahead.

Perhaps the implications for training are self-evident when one considers the above-mentioned contributions of biomedical scientists in a family planning program. I believe, however, that it will lend emphasis to the need if we delve in some depth into the story of current fertility control research.

The research can be divided into three categories. These are: applied research toward improvement of existing contraceptive methods, laboratory findings which may lead quickly to new contraceptive methods, and basic research on the reproductive processes.

In the category of the improvement of existing methods, let us consider the current work with ovulation-inhibiting steroid compounds and with intra-uterine devices.

With respect to the ovulation-inhibiting compounds, the oral progestins, there are three major objectives apparent: (1) a quest for compounds with greater potency, so that dosage requirements can be reduced; (2) the testing of the sequential therapy of estrogen and progestin, in order to reduce the over-all cost; and (3) the development of long-acting injectible progestins for contraception.

There are available at the present time seven Food and Drug Administration approved products, marketed by five different pharmaceutical companies, for prescription sale as oral contraceptives. These are as follows:

Manufac-turer	Trade Name	Progestin (in mg.)	Estrogen (in mg.)
G. D. Searle Co.	Enovid (10 mg.)	Norethynodrel 9.85	Mestranol 0.15
Ortho	Ortho-No-vum (10 mg.)	Norethindrone 10	Mestranol 0.06
G. D. Searle Co.	Enovid (5 mg.)	Norethynodrel 5	Mestranol 0.075
G. D. Searle Co.	Enovid-E	Norethynodrel 2.5	Mestranol 0.1
Syntex	Norinyl	Norethindrone 2	Mestranol 0.1
Ortho	Ortho-Novum	Norethindrone 2	Mestranol 0.1
Parke Davis	Norlestrin	Norethindrone ace-tate 2.5	Ethinyl estradiol 0.05

These companies and several others are seeking energetically to find analogues of norethynodrel and norethindrone which would retain the desired progestational activity at lower dosage levels. Some analogues are already under clinical trial and will soon be submitted by the sponsoring companies for FDA approval.

Also under extensive clinical trial is the procedure of administering an estrogen alone (usually mestranol or ethinyl estradiol) for approximately fifteen days followed by a progestin alone for the remaining five days of therapy. This technique takes advantage of the gonadotrophin-suppressing action of estrogen to inhibit ovulation secondarily, followed by the action of progestin to prevent irregular bleeding and to prepare the endometrium for menstruation. Thus, the normal menstrual periodicity can be simulated in a fashion similar to that achieved by the presently employed oral contraceptives. The cost can be reduced by eliminating the progestin through most of the cycle. I believe, however, that the management of the therapy will require a greater degree of sophistication by the supervising physician and that the prescribing of estrogen alone (not in combination with progesterone) is likely to be resisted by many medical people who, until now, have accepted the concept of combination steroid therapy.

Before turning from the use of steroids to control ovulation, it is perhaps pertinent to review current thinking with respect to their use to "regularize" the ovulatory cycle. As they are presently used on a schedule of twenty-days of pill taking starting from the fifth day after the beginning of the previous menstrual bleeding, the pills inhibit ovulation, eliminate the normal ovarian cycle, and replace it by the periodic bleeding occurring when the drug is withdrawn. A recent proposal is to prescribe the pill for "regularizing" the cycle by starting on day fifteen of a cycle and continuing daily for approximately ten days. Withdrawal bleeding would thus occur on day twenty-eight of the cycle, and the procedure would then be repeated. Theoretically the cycle would be "regularized" without suppressing ovulation. In this procedure, periodic abstinence could be practiced, with abstinence limited approximately to three or four days at mid-cycle and, theoretically, the successful use of "pill adjusted rhythm" would be much greater than "natural rhythm." The effectiveness of this proposed procedure has not yet been established with adequate evidence for statistical evaluation. The key to its success or failure lies in the effect of the drug sequence on the subsequent ovulation time. If it is hastened, as is possible, the method will not provide protection without extremely long periods of abstinence, and this would offer no improvement over "natural rhythm."

The use of long-acting injectible progestins for contraception is still in need of refinement. There is available now at least one injectible progestin which has a long-acting capacity, but the period of induced amenorrhea tends to be variable.

Research with intra-uterine devices has now been narrowed down to the questions of design, safety, and mode of action. Effectiveness, I believe, is no longer in doubt. As a result of a large number of studies all over the world, it is clear that several forms of intra-uterine devices are effective. Pregnancy rates of less than 2 pregnancies per 100 years of exposure have been achieved. Perhaps sometime in the future even these results will be improved upon, but it seems that the present rate of effectiveness is acceptable and certainly a tremendous improvement over most other means of contraception available. It is of further interest that the method is proving to have remarkable acceptability in countries all over the world. Use of the method is spreading in Korea, Taiwan, Japan, Chile, Puerto Rico, the United States, India, and Pakistan. In every country with family planning programs the method is proving to be acceptable and effective.

Much information has been accumulated relative to the safety of the method. Enough histological studies have been done to indicate that normal endometrial histology prevails when an intra-uterine device is used. There is no longer question about inducing alarming rates of pelvic inflammatory disease, as was feared when silver intra-uterine rings were first proposed by Gräfenberg. Pelvic inflammatory disease is, however, still being considered as a research question mainly because it is very difficult to establish what is the norm in a controlled population against which the incidence noted in intra-uterine device cases can be compared. However, on the basis of the evidence now accumulated in a study involving 10,000 women in the United States and in Puerto Rico, a pattern is evolving which indicates that the rate of pelvic inflammatory disease is about what would be expected in a normal population.

The questions of cancer and long-range effects will not be answered until long-range observations have been completed, but one does have an indication of early tendencies based on the studies of cervical exfoliative cytology. Until now there has been no evidence that the use of an intra-uterine device causes the cytological changes associated with cervical cancer.

Until very recently there was virtually no evidence whatsoever concerning the mode of action of intra-uterine devices. One could say, in a general way, that the method interfered with implantation, but this left a great range of possible activities to be explored.

Recently, preliminary reports were announced by Dr. Luigi Mastroianni, professor of obstetrics and gynecology, UCLA Medical School, covering his study of intra-uterine devices on rhesus monkeys of proven fertility which had been imported from India. This important study afforded, for the first time, an opportunity to study in primates events in the Fallopian tube for possible clues to the mechanism of action of intra-uterine devices. Dr. Mastroianni's results will be reported in detail by him elsewhere. Briefly, he has observed that within twenty-four hours after induced ovulation approximately 75 per cent of released ova can be recovered from the Fallopian tubes of normal control monkeys. Although ovulation occurs in device-bearing females, ova could not be recovered from the Fallopian tube. Dr. Mastroianni's preliminary observation, if confirmed and extended, implies that one of two things could be occurring. The egg, after achieving the Fallopian tube, could be passed very quickly through the tube so that it has made its exit in twenty-four hours. The normal period of passage of an egg through the Fallopian tube in the monkey, as in the human, is about four days. The other possibility is that the egg never entered the tube. Perhaps for some reason the movement of the ostial end of the tube to the ovary has been prevented, so that the egg has simply fallen into the peritoneal cavity. Interpretation of the results will have to await more extensive investigations. In the meanwhile, however, it appears that for one reason or another the egg is not in the tube twenty-four hours after ovulation.

Several laboratory findings are significant in the search for new methods of contraception even though they have not yet reached the stage of application in contraceptive methodology. There are, I believe, six important laboratory leads which might in the near future give rise to new practical applied methodology. These are: immuno-reproduction research, especially related to the immunology of sperma-tozoa; research on antizygotic compounds; work with antispermato-genic compounds; study of compounds with antiprogestational activity; the identification and purification of gonadotrophin-releasing fac-tors from the hypothalamus; and studies on the basic mechanism of hormone action.

The immunologic prospects have been discussed for many years. It is fully established that the antigenic properties of spermatozoa provide a basis to induce aspermatogenesis, the loss of spermatogenesis, through active immunization. This has been known since about 1954, when reported by Freund and his collaborators, and the fact that sperm are antigenic has been known since the last century. Recently, however, some progress has been made toward understanding of this phenome-non. Quite important, I believe, is the recent realization that the mechanism of the immunologic insult is through tissue bound antibod-ies and not by means of a general circulating antibody. This finding has been established by Dr. Kenneth Laurence at the Population Council laboratories. He has shown further that the immunologically induced aspermatogenesis is reversible, so that animals that have become completely azospermic can, after six to eight months, restore normal sperm counts. These are the two important new developments in the immunologic work.

The first reports on antizygotic compounds appeared in 1957, and we are still far from having new, applied contraceptive methodology developed from these initial observations. The main reason has been that although a large number of compounds having antizygotic activity have been uncovered in the laboratory, none has proved to have this activity at a dose without detrimental side effects when tested in the human. Nevertheless, the principle has been very definitely established that it is possible for some pharmacologic agents to have an effect on ova or on the transport of ova after fertilization and before implantation. In laboratory animals, if these compounds (there are now seven of them known) are administered between the time of fertilization and the time of implantation in the wall of the uterus, the fertilized ova degenerate. An activity of this type in the human would permit a retrospective kind of contraception that could be timed with coitus. A woman could take a pill for a day or two after coitus and if a fertilization had occurred, the zygote would not survive and the fertile cycle would go completely unnoticed, since the menstrual flow would appear on schedule.

Several compounds having antispermatogenic activity have been uncovered in the laboratory. But when tested in humans the element of toxicity has prevented the compounds from being given over to widespread use.

With more immediate possibilities are the prospects of the development of antiprogestational compounds. Such substances would interfere with the preparation of the endometrium for nidation of the fertilized egg. Several steroid analogues appear in laboratory animals to prevent the endometrial changes usually induced by endogenous progestins, and at least one of these compounds has now undergone adequate toxicity studies in the human to indicate that it could be taken safely in doses that have antiprogestational activity. Its contraceptive effectiveness remains to be established.

The last two topics to be considered, gonadotrophin-releasing factors and mechanism of hormone action are really in the realm of very basic research, but they are the kinds of studies that could very quickly lead to a breakthrough in fertility control methodology.

It is now quite clear that the hypothalamus produces secretions which control the rate of production of gonadotrophic hormones by the pituitary gland. These secretions are relatively small molecules, probably octapeptides. Biochemists are able to synthesize polypeptides of this size, so that once the gonadotrophin-releasing factors are, in fact, identified, they may be synthesized. Once they are synthesized, it seems likely that slightly altered analogues could be created which would inhibit the naturally produced substances.

Recently there have been important developments in the study of mechanism of hormone action. A line of work is developing which shows that the first identifiable chemical phenomenon when a hormone acts as a stimulation in the rate of protein synthesis in the target cell. This is heralded by an increase, and qualitative change, in the production of intra-nuclear RNA. This work is still in its early stages, but it holds great promise for the unraveling of the mystery of the hormones. And once we know how hormones act we shall be in a very much better position to try to interfere with this action.

With respect to training needs, the implications of this review are self-evident. The schools of public health, if they are to train people to work in family planning programs, will need to instruct them in the basics of reproduction physiology, so that these individuals can at least be conversant with the physiological mechanisms involved in the processes with which they are dealing.

18

Training of Professional Personnel for Work in Population Dynamics by Schools of Public Health

PAUL A. HARPER

Schools of public health have responsibility to train people for careers in public health or in research which is related to public health. The disciplines represented in the faculty and curriculum can be divided into three groups: the biological-medical, the statistical-epidemiologic, and the applied group, which comprises public health administration and its subspecialties, such as maternal and child health and mental hygiene. The social sciences may be considered to bridge the latter two groups or should be designated as a fourth group. Schools of public health thus have a pattern and tradition of bringing together people who are already well trained in such disciplines as biology, medicine, statistics, and the social sciences and preparing them to work together on some specific problem. The rapid growth of human populations may well tax the resources of all these disciplines.

The role that schools of public health will play in training for careers in population dynamics will be directly related to the degree of responsibility that official health agencies ultimately will take in population and family planning work around the world. This, in turn, will be greatly influenced by the amount of medical supervision required for the methods of contraception that will prove most successful in bringing family planning to segments of the population which do not now have it. Fertility regulation by so-called "conventional methods" requires relatively little medical supervision and has been quite successful in keeping birth and death rates in balance in countries which have favorable standards of living and education; public health agen-

203

cies have had little to do with family planning in such countries. But the conventional methods have had meager success in populations where literacy and living standards are low and where agriculture is the chief occupation. It currently appears that sophisticated methods which require careful medical supervision are most likely to succeed in these developing populations. Such methods include the intra-uterine devices, surgery for sterilization, and the oral contraceptives.

If some very simple and effective method is developed which does not require any health supervision and which can be distributed through commerical channels, then the role of the health agencies is likely to diminish. If, however, the methods of the future continue to demand a considerable degree of medical and health supervision, then the role of the health agencies is likely to be augmented.

The term "population dynamics" is used to comprise all aspects of population growth and fertility regulation. The training of professional personnel for work in population dynamics by schools of public health has developed largely as a response to the rapidly increasing demand for such training by students who are preparing to specialize in this work. For example, this School had only three students who might have been regarded as majors in this field during the nineteen-fifties; currently we have three times this number each year who come primarily for study of this subject.

Three parts of the problem will be discussed briefly: first, the extent of the potential demand for such training; second, the activities of the twelve schools of public health in the U.S. and Canada now engaged in this field; and finally, a few remarks on our present program and plans for the future at Hopkins.

It is desirable to define the potential trainees who would be admitted to and benefit from a year or more of work at a U.S.A. school of public health. These are the people who will have broad responsibility for, or special skills to contribute to, public programs of population dynamics. Most family planning workers in other countries will be trained in their own schools. Only those who are to be senior administrators, teachers, or research workers will be sent abroad. The potential trainees from both the U.S. and abroad can be grouped into a few categories: administrators, clinicians, demographers, physiologists, social scientists, and a few senior nurse-midwives. Most of these will have had their basic training in their own special schools and will come to a school of public health for advanced study of matters related to population growth and fertility regulation.

Potential Pool of Trainees in Population Dynamics

The schools of public health and interested agencies and foundations need to have estimates of the number of family planning workers and related research and teaching staff who would benefit from a year or more in a U.S. school of public health. Such estimates merely help to define the size of the potential pool of trainees; the actual number that will be sent will depend on the quality of training available and on the decisions of health departments, governments, and foundations to support such training.

Estimates are in two parts: (1) that which is concerned with the U.S. and Canada, and (2) that which deals with developing countries. The method of arriving at estimates of the pool of potential trainees in the U.S. and Canada has used the plans of The Johns Hopkins School of Hygiene and Public Health as a model for estimating need for personnel to staff a Division of Population Dynamics and then to multiply these estimates by five on the assumption that at least five of the twelve schools of public health will develop similar programs. Table 1 shows a

TABLE 1: ESTIMATES OF YEARS OF TRAINING TO
DEVELOP STAFF FOR DIVISION OF POPULATION
DYNAMICS AT A U.S. SCHOOL OF PUBLIC HEALTH

Category	Number	Training-Years
Administrator	1	x
Asst. administrator	1[a]	2
Physiologist	1	x
Asst. physiologist	1[a]	3
Demographer-biostatistician	1	x
Asst. demographer	1[a]	2
Behavioral scientist	1	x
Asst. behavioral scientist	1[a]	2
Full-time overseas advisers:		
Administrator	1[a]	2
Nurse-midwife	1[a]	1
Biostatistician	1[a]	2
Behavioral scientist	1[a]	1
[a] Needing training, total:	8	
Total person-years of training:		15

x No additional training anticipated.

projected staff of eight persons for a Division of Population Dynamics at Hopkins, plus four more full-time overseas workers or advisers, or a total of twelve persons, eight of who will need fifteen person-years of training. If this estimate of eight persons who will need fifteen person-years of training to provide the staff for one school is multiplied by five schools, we have forty persons who would need a total of seventy-five person-years of training and experience over the next five years, or fifteen persons in training each year.

Additional needs for the U.S. are based on the fact that most state and large city health departments are rapidly developing expanded programs of prenatal care and are also developing family planning services for their clinic clientele. The workers needed will be primarily obstetrical consultants, nurse-midwives, and health educators who will be responsible to develop better maternity health services which will include family planning or prepregnancy health care. Many of these workers will need training in public health with a major interest in population dynamics. Estimates have been made for the number of obstetrician-administrators currently needed in Maryland and in the District of Columbia, and these figures have been extrapolated to the nation. Thus the state of Maryland now employs one full-time obstetrician in the State Health Department and is recruiting for another. The Baltimore City Health Department has long had one half-time obstetrical consultant and has just added an additional full-time obstetrician-administrator. The District of Columbia also has one full-time obstetrical consultant. This gives a total of 4.5 obstetrical-gynecological administrator-consultants in health departments serving 4.5 million people, or one per 1 million. If this ratio of one public health obstetrician per 1 million population is applied across the nation, then this would represent 190 such consultants. If we assume that all of these 190 persons will be recruited and given public health-family planning training in the next ten years, then the number to be trained each year is 19. To this must be added a number to compensate for attrition. This is arbitrarily assumed to be seven per cent of those trained each year, or one the first year, three the second year, four the third year, etc., giving a total of about 75 over the ten-year period, or an average of seven per year. The total to be trained each year is then $19 + 7 = 26$.

A number of health educators and senior nurse-midwives will also need training; but since the number is unknown, and since it is very doubtful that obstetricians can be recruited at a rate of 26 per year, this additional need is included under the figure of 26 in the previous paragraph.

The potential pool of trainees from the United States is thus 15 for schools of public health plus 26 for official health agencies, or 41 per year (see summary Table 4).

The method of making estimates for developing countries is to use Pakistan as a model and to extrapolate the known needs of Pakistan to other countries which have adopted or appear on the verge of adopting official family planning programs.

Tables 2 and 3 show the senior staff of the family planning organization of the government of Pakistan who are potential candidates for overseas training. Table 2 gives details for the central government and subtotals for East and West Pakistan. Table 3 gives data for West Pakistan. The total number of senior staff currently employed in family planning is 53, and the person-years of training recommended is 59. The number to be trained each year for five years is $59 \div 5 = 12$, to which must be added an allowance for attrition. The latter is arbitrarily assumed to be seven per cent of those trained each year, or one the first year, two the second year, etc., giving a total of 12 over the five-year period, or an average of two per year. The total to be trained each year is then $12 + 2 = 14$.

The potential pool of 14 trainees each year from Pakistan with a population of 100 million approximates one trainee for about each 8 million persons per year. This figure is applied to the population of other developing countries which are similar to Pakistan in commitment to a family planning program and in development of their own educational system. These countries are listed as "Type 1" countries in Table 4. The need for overseas training may be less in countries with less commitment to a family planning program or where professional education is better developed and a factor of one overseas trainee per year to each 12 million population has been used to estimate the number of family planning workers who would benefit from overseas training in this second group of nations, "Type 2."

Table 4 also summarizes our estimates of the pool of workers in population dynamics who are potential candidates for training in U.S. schools of public health. The potential number of workers available for training each year is estimated at 94 from nine developing countries and 41 from the U.S., or a total of 135 per year. These estimates are high in that a few of the persons listed above will already have had overseas

TABLE 2: NUMBER OF YEARS OF OVERSEAS TRAINING RECOMMENDED FOR SELECTED FAMILY PLANNING WORKERS IN PAKISTAN

	Total Number Persons	Years of Training					
		Administrator Training Officer	Demographer-Statistician	Physiologist	Behavioral Scientist or Health Educator	Ob-Gyn Consultant	Lady Health Visitor-Social Worker
Central Government[a]							
Family planning officer	1	x					
Asst. F.P. officer	1	1					
National Res. Inst. F.P.							
Director	1	x					
Research officer	1	1					
Demographer	1		3				
Physiologist	1			3			
Behavioral scientist	1				1		
Subtotal, central govt.	7	2	3	3	1		
Subtotal, West Pakistan (from Table 3)	23	14	5	2	2	1	1
Subtotal, East Pakistan (needs assumed to be similar to those of West Pakistan)	23	14	5	2	2	1	1
Total for all Pakistan	53	30	13	7	5	2	2
Total person-years of training: 59							

[a] All positions currently budgeted or proposed in Third Five-Year Plan as of January 1, 1964.
x Not recommended for overseas training.

TABLE 3: NUMBER OF YEARS OF OVERSEAS TRAINING RECOMMENDED FOR SELECTED FAMILY PLANNING WORKERS IN WEST PAKISTAN

	Total Number Persons	Years of Training		
		Administrator Training Officer	Demographer-Statistician	Other
WEST PAKISTAN:[a]				
Family planning officer	1	x		
Asst. F.P. officer	1	1		
Statistician	1		3	
Health educator	1			1
Training-cum-research inst.— Lahore:				
Director (also of MESOREP)	1	x		
Asst. director—training	1	1		
Statistician	1		2	
Lady health visitor	1			1
Physiologist	1			2
MESOREP:				
Director	1	1		
Associate director	1	1		
Gynecologist	1			1
Behavorial scientist	1			1
Training-cum-research inst.— Hyderabad:				
Lady medical officer	1	1		
Regional family planning officers	6	6		
Principals of lady health visitor schools	3	3		
Total for West Pakistan	23	14	5	6

[a] All positions provided as in footnote Table 2, except director and physiologist of the training-cum-research institute, Lahore.

x Not recommended for overseas training.

training; others will not wish to leave home or will not be released by their governments. Also, some of the countries will develop strong domestic training programs. This tendency to overestimate will be compensated in part by the fact that other countries from Asia, Africa, and Latin America can be expected to develop family planning programs and to have need for trained personnel.

It is worth repeating that these estimates merely serve to put a crude number on the pool of potential trainees and that there is a substantial need for the sort of training which we are discussing.

TABLE 4: POOL OF WORKERS IN POPULATION
DYNAMICS AVAILABLE FOR TRAINING IN
U.S. SCHOOLS OF PUBLIC HEALTH

Developing Countries	Potential Number of Persons for Training per Year	
Type 1 (1 candidate per 8 million population[a]):		
Pakistan	14	
India	65	
Thailand	4	
Tunisia	1	
United Arab Republic	4	
Type 2 (1 candidate per 12 million population[a]):		
Turkey	2	
Korea	2	
Taiwan	1	
Ceylon	1	94
U.S.A.:[b]		
Public health faculty, including consultants for overseas work	15	
Official Health Agencies: Obstetric-gynecological consultants, health educators, nurse-midwives	26	41
Total		135

[a] See text for derivation of this ratio.
[b] See text for derivation of estimates for U. S.

Current Programs in Population Dynamics in Schools of Public Health

The data to be presented here on current programs of teaching and research in population dynamics in U.S. and Canadian schools of public health is being gathered by the professors of maternal and child health in the various schools. All schools give courses in biostatistics, public health administration, and health education; nine schools have electives in research design and survey methods; two have courses about the factors influencing the growth of populations, with illustrations largely from lower animals. Most of these courses are basic in nature and are not focused on the problem of rapid growth of human populations. All of the training is at the graduate level, and in many schools it is largely at the postdoctoral level.

There is great variation among the schools in the availability of courses directly related to population dynamics. All schools have occasional lectures or seminars on this subject, nine schools have courses in demography, and six have some teaching in the physiology of fertility regulation. Other offerings are largely limited to four schools which have programs of teaching and research that are designed for "majors" in population. The core courses in population at these schools and the range in hours allotted are shown in Table 5. The course descriptions in Table 5 are purposely broad in order to allow the

TABLE 5: CORE COURSES IN POPULATION DYNAMICS AT
FOUR U.S. SCHOOLS OF PUBLIC HEALTH WITH
MAJOR PROGRAMS

Subject	Total Clock Hours— Range in Four Schools
Demography—(methodology)	10–75
Population growth—interrelations, social and economic determinants, problems and policies in comparative international focus (substantive demography)	24–64
Family planning programs— at national, state, and community level—planning, staffing, operation, records, evaluation	10–58
Physiology of fertility regulation	10–24
Other—tutorial, etc.	(not estimated)

offerings of the various schools to be grouped in a few categories. One or two other schools have announced plans to develop similar programs for majors in the near future.

Three schools reported a total of fourteen students "majoring in population" for the year 1963–64. Most of these were physicians; about three-quarters were from overseas.

Several schools have plans to develop a faculty group which will concentrate on teaching and research in population dynamics. It is therefore probable that the curriculum offerings of several schools will be expanded both in content and in depth beyond that shown in Table 5.

Current Program at Hopkins and Plans for the Future

The description of the current curriculum at Hopkins can be summarized rapidly because much of this two-day program is illustrative of the type of material which is presented. Table 6, part A, gives the current core courses for majors in population at Hopkins and part B lists the additions that are currently planned.

Before proceeding further it may be desirable to look critically at our current training as listed in part A of Table 6. We believe that these courses provide a solid foundation. The overseas research program in Pakistan (page 35) has added substantially to our experience and to the teaching.

However, this is only a beginning. There is much room for improvement. All of the Hopkins-based faculty who have participated in this work have had other major responsibilities. No new full-time staff has been added in Baltimore. There has not been enough individual attention to students and only two of our major students have been able to stay longer than the one-year minimum.

Additional highly qualified faculty must be recruited. All trainees should work closely with senior faculty who are actively engaged in teaching and research. More emphasis should be put on advanced training for a small group of perhaps six to eight trainees each year. Each such trainee should work as an apprentice to a senior faculty member.

Two or three new subject matter areas need to be added to the present curriculums. One is the physiology of fertility regulation. A beginning has been made this year with a series of seminars given by visiting lecturers, but there is need for a highly qualified physiologist to organize a laboratory, a training program, and research in this area. This would benefit all our students, but the greatest gain would be for a few postdoctoral workers to specialize in research and teaching.

The second subject area will be concerned with a variety of factors which influence people to practice or reject family planning. It will also deal with the organization of services to reach the families in each community. There needs to be more emphasis on the sociologic and psychologic factors which motivate behavior and on how to communicate with people who need information. There also needs to be more attention to the organization of family planning services. The principles of public health and business administration need to be applied to

TABLE 6: CORE COURSES FOR MAJORS IN POPULATION AT HOPKINS, 1963–64 [a]

Title	Department	Number in Most Recent Class	Lecture	Seminar	Laboratory
A. Currently Available					
Demography	Biostatistics	13	+		+
Fertility, Sterility, and Child Spacing	Maternal and Child Health	16		+	
Introduction to Maternal and Child Health, Mental Health and International Health	Maternal and Child Health, Mental Hygiene and International Health	30	+	+	
Public Health Statistics: Application of Scientific Methods to Solve Public Health Problems	Biostatistics and Maternal and Child Health	18	+		+
Biology of Populations: Inherited and Environmental Factors Affecting the Growth of Animal Populations	Pathobiology	53	+		+
Population Growth: The Influence of Social, Economic and Political Factors on Population Growth and National Policies	Division of Population Dynamics and International Health	20	+	+	
Health Education	Public Health Administration	7	+	+	
Seminar on Population	Division of Population Dynamics	4		+	
B. To Be Developed					
Physiology of Fertility Regulation	Division of Population Dynamics				
Local Programs of Family Planning	Division of Population Dynamics				
Summer Work [b]	Division of Population Dynamics				

[a] Those who are candidates for the Master of Public Health degree are also required to take a general course in each of the following: biostatistics, epidemiology, environmental medicine, and public health administration.

[b] Summer work is arranged to meet the needs of each person.

programs of fertility regulation. In all of these matters, teaching will come alive in direct proportion to the involvement of faculty in research in these problems.

To do these things, this University is seeking support for and proposes to establish a new Division of Population Dynamics with a multidisciplinary staff to devote full time to this work on the Hopkins home campus and also to develop a continuing affiliation with one or more overseas institutions engaged in teaching and research.

The purpose of the new Division will be to develop training and research of the highest quality and to prepare administrators, clinicians, demographers, physiologists, social scientists, and others for careers in this area.

A basic group of four new professorships is planned—one each in demography, physiology, public health administration, and sociology. There also will be a second faculty member and one or two postdoctoral fellows in each of these disciplines. Additional faculty, part or full time, will be needed from such disciplines as anthropology, economics, obstetrics and gynecology, health education, and communication.

The trainees will be divided into two groups. The largest group will be those who come for the basic training in public health with population dynamics as their major subject; most of this group will be here for one year. From them and from other sources will be gathered a smaller group of population dynamics fellows who will remain for advanced study, each working in close personal relationship with a member of the senior faculty.

The degree of specialization required will vary with the discipline. Ranked from most highly specialized to least, the order might be physiologist, demographer, social scientist, and administrator. The administrators will tend to be generalists and will require a variety of skills, including a medical background and many of the organizational abilities which make for success in administrative work or business. These will include a knowledge of the epidemiologic and statistical approaches to problem solving, judgment, ability to make decisions and accept responsibility, skill in personal communication and in interpersonal relations, and strong motivation to succeed. Most of these qualities will have been developed before arrival and are mentioned merely to emphasize their importance to those who are responsible for selection of fellows. What the School can and should do is to strengthen these attributes generally and, specifically, to foster an analytic approach to problems. Each senior fellow will participate in the research and teaching program of his senior faculty adviser. But his chief task will usually be to formulate some question or problem and to plan, carry out, analyze, and report on the studies.

This will be a co-operative effort by persons from six departments and three schools of the University. These are the Departments of Biostatistics, Environmental Medicine (physiology), Maternal and Child Health, and Public Health Administration—International Health of this School; the Department of Gynecology and Obstetrics of the Medical School, and the Department of Social Relations of the Faculty of Philosophy. These departments have a tradition of successful co-operation which is facilitated by joint appointments and joint courses. This development should significantly improve and expand the University's capacity to contribute to research and teaching in population dynamics.

19

Discussion of Papers 16–18

MOYE W. FREYMANN

CHAIRMAN STEBBINS: Dr. Freymann will open the discussion. He presented a very interesting paper the first morning of the Conference, and we know of his great interest in the training of personnel for population programs.

FREYMANN: Dr. Kirk asked a question: Is there a discrete discipline which could properly be called "family planning program development," or some such name? I would assert that there is a growing body of knowledge and technique that do form such an entity and that this entity will occupy a major position in the field of public health in the future.

To defend this thesis, I would like first to present a brief sketch of what may be called the "genealogy" of an applied discipline. Let us use internal medicine as an illustration, a discipline which aims at helping to cure disease in individual patients. The fundamentals of this discipline are drawn from fields such as anatomy, physiology, biochemistry, and pathology. But elements of these fields are integrated at a more applied level by still other bodies of knowledge and of observational techniques, including the fields of physical diagnosis and therapeutics. It is at a still higher level of integration of elements of all these fields, with a focus on certain practical objectives, that we finally emerge with the entity we call internal medicine.

The field we have been calling family planning program development grew out of the basic sciences of demography and statistics, epidemiology, the social sciences, reproductive biology, and the medical sciences. Added to these, then, are the more applied fields of public health administration and education. Elements of all the component fields are then focused on the goal of promoting rational reproduction in human groups.

Dr. Guttmacher has traced the history of terms relating to this field.

217

The most current of these, "family planning," is excellent for public relations purposes; this term will probably persist as the name for community action programs to promote birth control. However, it is quite inadequate as a scientific term. A number of people have been groping for an alternative, something that would be more appropriate for a new academic department. Some proposed alternatives are lugubrious or diffuse. The term should allow for the broad scope of this new field and should be appropriate for a discipline having a sound scientific basis as well as a value-oriented ultimate goal.

Francis Galton made a good try in 1890 when he invented the word "eugenics." His original intent was that this would refer to the improvement of the human biologic stuff, but it would be legitimate to expand the term, perhaps making it "population eugenics," to allude to the quantitative as well as the qualitative aspects. Unfortunately, though, eugenics seems to be a term spoiled by bad usage; one friendly critic has commented that it "smacks of the 30's, with a faint odor of the Third Reich."

There are other alternatives. You might say "population research and administration," but the word "population" itself is unnecessarily vague. We are not primarily concerned in this field with mortality control or with the dynamics of migration but with reproduction. For this, "genics" is a good root to keep.

Ideally, we should add to "genics" a prefix which would connote an improvement, or change, or adjustment of reproduction to other factors in the environment. One which seems appropriate is "meta," as in metamorphosis or metastasis, implying movement or change. "Meta" is also used in another relevant sense in the word "metalinguistics." This term refers to the mutual relationships between language and the environment in which it exists.

These considerations lead to the proposal that "metagenics" be used as a more precise term for the discipline concerned with the art and science of family planning program development. I must refer, therefore, to the "complete metagenician" as the ideal product of the proposed new Division at Johns Hopkins.

Now, to the thoughtful papers that we have just heard. Dr. Kirk, I think, helped a lot in distinguishing the modes of application of social research to the field of metagenics. He referred, firstly, to the macrocosmic approaches of classical demographic research, which can help to identify the broad problem, its relationships to economic development, and so on; secondly, to survey research, more microcosmic studies aimed at further dissection of population problems; and thirdly, to studies on the evaluation of action programs. These three levels represent historical planes of development; they have advanced in proportion to their duration of existence. The third plane of development, that of measurement and evaluation of program effects, is really a tremendously challenging new frontier for the social researcher.

The problems of devising sensitive methods to detect changes in fertility patterns, so that one can quickly and efficiently assess possible effects of an operational program, are practically untouched. Also untouched are the problems of getting reliable and sensitive instruments for detecting trends over time in family size norms or of measuring small differences between different groups of people in relevant attitudes or even in consumption of contraceptives. If social scientists can help with such tools, we can more efficiently learn from experience with family planning programs.

I would like to ask Dr. Kirk, however, about the assumption sometimes made that the social scientist is the scientific educator and that if you know social science you know education. Certainly, insights into social dynamics provide an essential base for education; but isn't there a body of knowledge and skill which relates to the effective application of such insights? If so, should not the applied field of education deserve major representation in a division of metagenics and a program of family planning?

Dr. Segal has done us all a service in reviewing advances in the biomedical aspects of reproduction. As many of you know, Dr. Segal is not only a laboratory scientist; he also has a remarkable experience in development of action programs. I would like, therefore, to state a proposition for his comment, on the basis of what he knows about the problems of training in the U.S. and abroad for the field of metagenics. The proposition is that if a U.S. school of public health wants to contribute to the field of metagenics through research and teaching, it should make a decision to select a target population in its own area—a political entity such as the state, county, or city—and itself act as a catalyst to bring the achievement in that population of a certain goal; the goal might be broadly stated at the outset as the adoption of rational reproduction habits by all those in the population.

This would mean that the school of public health faculty should actually, itself, go through the discipline of helping to plan, develop, and evaluate a family planning program effort. It would mean, for example, that the concerned faculty would have to face the question of defining the criteria of need for family planning services. They would have to help with attempts to quantify the prevalence of people who meet such criteria in the population and with further studies of the dynamics of their problems. There would be need also for studies to identify the resources available to help to bring change to such groups and need for consultation and training to help these resources relate to the problem. A school of public health that goes through this exercise would be much more qualified to advise other agencies, here and abroad. It would be enriched itself by the variety of research activities so generated and by the experience gained by its staff.

Dr. Harper gave an extremely stimulating presentation of possible plans at Johns Hopkins in the field of metagenics. I was pleased by his reference to needs for relating to training institutions abroad. It would be improper for schools of public health in the U.S. to carry the burden of basic education in this field for people of other countries for a long period. The goal must be to work oneself out of this function as quickly as possible, by helping to build better training institutions abroad.

I would like to ask for Dr. Harper's thoughts on the general relationship of family planning programs to the field of maternal and child health. I wonder whether an occasional tendency to lump these two fields together may arise, in part, from the feminist origins of the family planning movement. Obviously, there are great potential benefits from association with maternal and child health services: this sanctifies the field, provides a very important avenue of approach to families, helps to generate financial support, and so on. However, the field of metagenics is much broader than the classical range of activities and concepts of maternal and child health; in some areas the main focus of family planning program activities may be on males, according to the needs of the local situation. In many countries maternal and child health services have not yet been able to reach a large proportion of the population and will not be able to for decades. An assumption that family planning must be only a part of the maternal and child health program can therefore be a serious barrier to progress.

I would welcome discussion also on how metagenics and family planning can be established clearly as a major frontier of public health in the future and on how to attract new people to this career line. What can be done, symbolically, to give it equal status with nutrition and environmental sanitation, maternal and child health, and other of the basic program fields in public health?

CHAIRMAN STEBBINS: Thank you very much, Dr. Freymann. Dr. Kirk.

KIRK: Dr. Freymann asks if there is a body of knowledge on how to motivate people. There is, of course. But, as I said in my presentation, the "hard sell" has never been tried in this field. I am not at all sure that it should be, but it has not been tried in any case. My own judgment is that what is needed is education more than motivation. In fact, I think it is even a nice moral question to ask whether it is our business or the business of people advancing family planning programs to try to convince people of the great virtues of family planning unless it really grows out of their own life-situation and their own judgment of what is good for them. I have confidence that people are basically very rational everywhere in the world and that if they are given the basic facts and services, they will form their own judgment and take advantage of family planning. I am not at all sure that we can play God or should play God in this field.

PANIAGUA: Chairman Stebbins, I wonder if we might not continue for a moment with the question of motivation. One way we phrase this problem in Puerto Rico is how to account for overachievement. We had identified that the ideal family size was smaller than the actual number of children born to mothers. It looks as if the attitudes were right, which is one indicator of motivation, but as Dr. Stycos put it, the acceptors were "right" only if they did not have to exert any effort at all, if somehow or other the methods could be applied without taking the necessary moves to make contacts. But the attitudes were not strong enough to actually carry them through.

We found it took relatively little in the civil program to get them started, but the commitment to continue, to persevere using the methods then available to them, was not strong enough without quite a bit of encouragement.

This takes issue a bit with the notion that information is enough. In the surveys it was found that the people had knowledge of birth control and that their attitudes were favorable toward it, but they had practiced it so little that, in actual family size, the difference between those who had practiced birth control and those who had not in the first ten years of marriage was only a fraction. So having the information and having a favorable attitude were not enough together to produce that amount of birth control use that was necessary, given the methods available at that time. So it looks as if the issue is not necessarily imposing one's values but rendering the problem sufficiently salient and timing your campaign correctly, if you are going to get action that will make a difference, even with respect to the individual's definition of proper family size.

Now that, I think, is somewhat different from a distinction, say, between motivation and education. The motivation has to be heightened; that is, you are not necessarily changing people's minds, but you are sharpening, so to speak, the issue and making it possible for them to take action.

This may be what Dr. Kirk means by the "hard sell," but the "hard sell" to me is changing the minds of people, shifting their direction, selling them things they don't really want, and we have not yet mounted a stimulus strong enough to make any substantial difference in our experimental work in any of the studies that I am acquainted with. The one that was reported to us by Dr. Bernard Berelson may actually constitute a first in this respect.

KIRK: I think actually there are several studies where it is quite clear that the programs of introducing family planning have influenced people to much greater acceptance of family planning than they had previously. I mentioned the Taiwan study, the Korean study, etc. I am afraid we are getting back into the old problem of semantics of what plans are we talking about when we talk about motivation. I confess I was reacting to the idea of trying to sell people something they might not really want.

I think that now when the realistic possibilities of adopting family planning are brought to people's attention, services are nearby and the methods are easier than those that you had to deal with in Puerto Rico at the time you were working. It is my judgment that you do not have to work very hard on persuading. What you do basically is inform people of the possibility and of the means that are hopefully relatively near at hand, cheap, and easy for them to get and to use.

PANIAGUA: I think maybe I am introducing a commitment which does not take place by itself. The facts presented do not bring about commitment, and there has to be some intermediate experience to bring it about; that is so relevant to training because we have done so little really in our educational programs in training people and bringing about commitment. It is this dimension of the problem, added to the notion of proper motivation, that I am suggesting here.

KIRK: I think we are coming into quite a different era in this business with these new techniques. The problem becomes quite different from that with which you were confronted. It seems quite difficult to keep up with technology in this field. Take the intra-uterine devices. Suddenly the medical profession looms very large in this picture, because at least in the present situation, the intra-uterine devices must be, according to medical opinion, inserted by medical people or at least by trained people. From the point of view of the woman concerned, the whole problem of continuing motivation disappears, because once the device is in place and remains in place this problem does not exist.

CHAIRMAN STEBBINS: It is commitment.

KIRK: Well, it is initial commitment. Yes. I think we are admittedly in a field in which we are all groping, but the kind of problem that you were confronted with in Puerto Rico may not be characteristic of the problems that will be encountered by those using the new methods.

ELIOT: I do not see either Dr. Peng or Dr. Berelson here, and I know that Dr. Freedman has very strong feelings on this subject. If he heard the Taiwan work referred to as an exception in this regard, I think he would be most distressed. It is his distinct credo that they are helping people to do what people want to do. They are not in there to brainwash anyone.

PANIAGUA: It was not in that respect that I was calling it an exception. It was a success.

LEAVELL: Mr. Chairman, I wonder if we have not been skirting around Dr. Freymann's principle a little bit. He has education listed as one of the parents of metagenics, and I take it if there had been a practitioner of educational methods in the audience, he or she would probably have spoken out. It seems to me what he was saying was that we need to add to the group a practitioner of the body of knowledge that Dr. Kirk spoke about—what is apparently being called a scientific educator. Is this the question that you are raising, Dr. Freymann?

FREYMANN: There is a body of skills and concepts which is the object, for example, of a new unit proposed to be set up at Michigan. It is tentatively called CRUSK, the Center for Research on the Utilization of Knowledge. The skills pertaining to the application of basic knowledge are partly represented in public health by the field of health education. So far, one of the main lessons that may be learned from action research experiments in family planning is that social scientists may be very poor educators. It has been a main problem of such efforts to get educational skills into the initial planning.

CHAIRMAN STEBBINS: Dr. Segal, you had some questions thrown at you.

SEGAL: I do have some thoughts on the role of U.S. schools of public health in developing proper training. I wonder how a school of public health can take on the responsibility of training family planning workers or administrators if the institution itself is not in the actual process of doing this very thing?

A man who is faced with the implementation of a family planning program in his own country, many instances of which will occur in the near future, is faced with starting from scratch with the identification of the problem, even to the extent, as Dr. Freymann said, of defining the population with which he is going to work—defining the people who need the service and not simply taking for granted that there are people there and that those who want the service will get it.

In the foreign programs that Dr. Harper referred to, that would be in conjunction with the new Division of Population Dynamics. The people on the Hopkins faculty who will work in these programs will have certain areas of decision already made for them. They are going to be advisers in ongoing foreign programs. It will practically be defined for them from the outset, at least in general terms, what the country intends to do. Then these advisers will participate in carrying things from there.

These advisers are then going to come back and become the faculty to train the pool of people described by Dr. Harper. How different is this from the kind of proposition that Dr. Freymann proposes?

As I understand it, and I think I agree fully with him, if a school of public health takes on the responsibility of doing something in an area in this country, we have plenty of areas right around Baltimore where good family planning programs of the Korean or Taiwan type are needed. But then how do you decide on which people are going to be serviced in this area? It is not simply a matter of deciding on the basis of what the community will allow you to do, because the Welfare Department says you can only give health services to women who are married and living with their husbands and have three children and so on, which is not really solving the problem.

Even if it means combating these forces that might oppose you, religious and political, this is part of the problem that you have to learn how to work out. How do you overcome these oppositional forces? How do you make decisions in the framework of the possible opposition?

Once you have done that, you have to go down the line for clinic services and for other extension services. You make the decision, set up the administration to implement it, and work out a family planning program of so-called underdeveloped style in the United States, where there is really a great need for such programs.

People who go through this exercise will have a lot of answers when they come to the teaching platform in their capacity as faculty members in the Division of Population Dynamics. At the same time, these ongoing programs would serve as excellent laboratories for the students enrolled in the program.

CHAIRMAN STEBBINS: Dr. Polgar.

POLGAR: I would like to add a comment to what Dr. Segal said in case anybody here thinks that this proposition will meet any opposition from Planned Parenthood. Dr. Guttmacher is gone, so I suppose I could take it upon myself to speak for their national organization. Perhaps Dr. Trimble from Maryland will say something after I do.

Let me just mention that I myself have been working out of the national office for Planned Parenthood. In the last few months, I have gone to Dean Snyder of Harvard and told him that when he gets his program going we would like to have him send his students to work with us. Also, I have gone to Dean Trussell, and we have some concrete plans afoot to have Columbia evaluate a mobile unit project in New York. I am sure Dr. Eliot can speak for the collaboration between Planned Parenthood in Detroit and the University of Michigan. In other words, the proposal being made by Dr. Freymann and Dr. Segal is not entirely illusory but is something that we of Planned Parenthood would welcome.

TRIMBLE: I would like to say that the Eastern Health District, in which this School is located, is pitifully served with family planning services, and I know Planned Parenthood, for one, would be just delighted if the Hopkins School would show a little more guidance to the people in this area.

CHAIRMAN STEBBINS: I will let Dr. Harper comment on this.

HARPER: Dr. Trimble and other people in the Planned Parenthood group have been most generous in helping with our teaching program and are taking major responsibility for the course entitled "Fertility, Sterility and Child Spacing." They have also urged us to participate with them in evaluating the family planning programs that are being developed in this state, and we have indicated that we would be delighted to do this but that we need some more people.

Dr. Freymann asked whether or not family planning services should be a part of maternal and child health services. I have already made the point that the future role of official health agencies in family planning work will be largely influenced by the amount of medical supervision needed to promote those methods of contraception that future experience will show to have been most successful in reducing birth rates in groups that now have high birth rates. It is my view that if family planning services are to be the responsibility of the public health agency, then they should be part of other general preventive health services. The reasons for this are partly psychological and partly administrative. The public image and chances for acceptance of family planning services are likely to be improved if they are presented as part of a general plan to improve the health and well-being of mothers and children, rather than simply as a contraceptive service. Similarly, the broader concept is favorable to good esprit in the professional staff. The methods of contraception which call for continued medical supervision (currently including the oral tablets and the intra-uterine devices) are both directed at women, and it would therefore seem to be administratively desirable to make these family planning services a part of the maternal health services in countries where they have well-organized prenatal and postpartum health services.

In countries where there is no specialized maternal health service, it would seem desirable to make the family planning services a part of the general health services. I realize that this argument does not take account of the fact that sterilization of males is a small but important part of the family planning armamentarium. Perhaps the term "maternal and child health services" should be changed to "family health services."

Assuming that there will continue to be a need for health supervision of contraceptors by medically trained personnel, then it would clearly be undesirable to set up a separate service for family planning outside the official health agency. This would lead to competition for scarce medical personnel, to jurisdictional conflicts, and to much duplication of effort. These problems would be avoided under an administration where family planning services would be part of the work of the official health agency.

CHAIRMAN STEBBINS: Dr. Mendoza.

MENDOZA: I have a question for Dr. Harper. You say you include all the specialists. From the experience that we have already in family planning we know the social worker has played a tremendous role. When the social worker fails to play his role, the program is usually damaged. I do not see any place where you have the social worker included.

HARPER: I have added it to the list. I would quite agree. I think the social worker, the educator, and the nurse-midwife are part of the family planning team.

TRIMBLE: In connection with that question, what are the social sciences that you have included there?

HARPER: I just looked over Dr. Berelson's book a few days ago, and he defines the behavioral scientist as including primarily the sociologist, the anthropologist, and the psychologist, but there are also certain groups of economists and historians and various others.

KIRK: May I make one observation on Dr. Harper's paper? It is an interesting coincidence. In one of his tables he suggests that the potential number of persons for training per year from Pakistan might be fourteen. I trust this is not collusion. The government of Pakistan is indeed sending fourteen people this year for training in the United States in the field of family planning. In other words, I have evidence of the realism of his estimate.

HARPER: I wonder how this looks to India, where, using that same method, we get the tremendous number of sixty-four or sixty-five.

CHAIRMAN STEBBINS: Dr. Gonzalez?

GONZALEZ: I want to take advantage of Dr. Freymann and suggest the term "reproductive anthropology."

RAO: The way I understand it should be either "biogenics" or "homogenics," or one of these species.

CHAIRMAN STEBBINS: Dr. Balfour, you have been very quiet.

BALFOUR: I was thinking about Dr. M. Freymann's ambition to create a new word, metagenics. I wish him luck. The only way to succeed in such an effort is to keep driving at it for ten years or more. I recall when I was a malariologist that I tried to promote the use of the word "endemo-epidemicity," which seemed to describe a particular disease condition. Well, the Greeks liked it because they understood the word. It has never become popular in epidemiology.

I won't say anything about Dr. Paul Harper's tables and his estimate of future needs of personnel beyond suggesting that they may represent an exercise in futility. Of course it is necessary at times to make such estimates and to arrive at some numbers. I am inclined to take things gradually and to deal in smaller numbers. It is a little like trying to project the population for the year 2000. The important thing is to make a beginning.

Lastly, in reference to the types of people that are needed in a public health school, I will accept the four or the eight who are proposed for the population field. In Boston they will probably give them different labels. Whether they are administrators, public health demographers, social scientists, or physiologists, to my way of thinking, the people are more important than their titles. It may seem trite to say it, but no plan is better than the people who are available to carry it out. I am more interested in specific individuals and their caliber than I am in their titles.

SEGAL: I notice at Boston they have got a theologian listed.

KAPRIO: I would like to make one observation. I think there are two types of situations when we think about the countries which may need support. One is a set of countries which already have a relatively large group of medical personnel of various types. The other is a group of countries which may, sometime in the future, be looking for all of us and come into this technical assistance program.

I think it is quite important to realize that we should think from the beginning about the teaching institutions, including not only the schools of public health but also the medical institutions which have the capabilities of medical education. We have been discussing the tremendous number of various types of foreign students who are studying in this country in various medical institutions. I think at every school of medicine there should be a professor of gynecology and obstetrics who would teach all the facts of life to the medical students, so that they can form their own opinions about different situations, whatever the policy of the country regarding population, abortions, and so on might be. We have seen in this country that schools of public health do quite progressive health work for any field in the world. But when you go next door to the medical school, you do not find quite the same approach to the problems.

CHAIRMAN STEBBINS: Thank you, Dr. Kaprio. Dr. Sadik?

SADIK: I would like to ask Dr. Segal what he thinks about the insertion of intra-uterine devices by paramedical personnel? Women only go to female doctors, and we have few of those in our country.

SEGAL: This question has come up frequently and I have an answer for you. It may change in the future. I do not believe that there is any need to turn to paramedical personnel now because, as far as I know, nowhere at the present level of acceptance and utilization of the IUD is there a block to the insertion of devices because of the lack of availability of physicians to do it.

Sometime in the future such a block may occur, but it is my judgment that it will be a mistake to try to press this concept upon the medical profession. By the time it develops that there is a need for more hands, especially feminine hands, to insert the devices, I feel certain that the medical profession will be so bored with inserting tens of thousands of these things that they will be very happy to train paramedical personnel; this would become a gradual transition rather than something imposed by a pressure group upon a group with special interests.

Since this question has arisen, I would like to emphasize something that has happened in Korea and that has perhaps been overlooked in the general picture of the Korean program. The Korean program has been excellent in the way they have handled the question of who does insertions. The training of physicians for insertion of these devices has started at the top, with the specialist in obstetrics and gynecology. It is my feeling, after talking with Dr. Yang, that before the training will be extended to the nonspecialist, every specialist, every obstetrician and gynecologist in Korea will have had the opportunity to add this skill to the armamentarium of his specialty. I think this is a very good way to go about it: Start with the men who think they own the pelvis, and when they feel that this is part of their particular specialty, then let them participate in the training of general physicians, and I think that it will broaden beyond that.

SADIK: Another question. What do we do in the meantime while we do not have sufficient health services? Suppose you introduce intra-uterine devices by medical personnel and then are not able to have a follow-up, what do you think would happen?

SEGAL: I do not think that the time has yet come for insertions of intra-uterine devices under those circumstances. I think that at the present level of experience and understanding of the devices their use should be restricted to those situations where some degree of medical follow-up is available. Now, this to me sounds like the more important area in which to consider the use of paramedical personnel. Village *dais* or other trained midwives could be used to take out rather than put in devices, and this might serve the purpose of supplementing the medical services available.

MURAMATSU: One question to Dr. Segal. On the basis of the observation you were describing, do you think we can say that the IUD is not an abortifacient?

SEGAL: Well, it depends on whom you put the burden of proof. I think that it would be impossible to prove that it is an abortifacient. In fact it might even depend on how you define abortion. Everyone has his or her own personal definition. I would like to defend the position, if you want me to do so. You cannot have an abortion until you have an implantation, and on that basis I think there is no question but that we can say the device is not an abortifacient, because there is ample evidence that implantation never occurs. If implantation had occurred there would be a prolongation of the cycle, but in the 780,000 cycles recorded in one particular study there was no evidence of a prolongation of cycle length.

CHAIRMAN STEBBINS: If there are no further questions I think we will adjourn. I want to thank the members of the panel, the discussants, and all of the participants.

This has been a very useful and productive two days for us in developing our plans for the program of population control, and we are very grateful to all of you for being here. Thank you.

Population and Public Health Policy

LEONA BAUMGARTNER *

Today's interest and concern about population movements and changes are not accidental, nor are they artifacts created by publicists. They are, instead, a recognition of one of the hardest of the hard realities of our time—the rapid rate of population growth, particularly in many countries struggling for modernization and independence. This growth is so rapid that it may slow or even prevent economic development itself. Despite the efforts made by many countries today, the gap between the haves and have-nots widens.

The magnitude of these problems of population growth is easily seen, for example, in Latin America, as it is now and as it may be by 1975. This, I would remind you, is not a remote future. The year 1960 was four years ago; the year 1975 is eleven years ahead. The population in 1975 is likely to be half again as large as it was in 1960, making an increase of 50 per cent in only fifteen years. There will be 60 per cent more children of elementary school age in 1975 than in 1960. Schools and teachers must be provided for children not now in school—and expansion must be rapid enough to provide for ever-increasing numbers. Numbers of men in the working ages are increasing by 15 per cent every five years. There are three persons reaching labor force age for each one who leaves. Employment is a crucial problem, economic as well as political. New families formed in 1975 may be 60 per cent more numerous than those formed in 1960, and so another problem now acute becomes compounded—that of housing. Increasing savings and capital investments are difficult when more than 50 per cent of the total population is below fifteen years of age. Given such dimensions, the

* Assistant Administrator for Technical Cooperation and Research, Agency for International Development.

problem of population growth and its essential relations to economic and social development in Latin America are evident.

Given the facts of population growth in the developing countries not only in Latin America, but in Asia, Africa, and the islands of the several seas, we should perhaps explain the reasons for the delayed recognition of these problems of population. It is not as if population changes have not frequently influenced history in the past. Witness the plagues of the Middle Ages and their relation to the economic and spiritual depression of those days. Or the availability of Swiss soldiers for wars in many lands, which was associated with the imbalance of the numbers of Swiss people and the natural resources they could command to support themselves. Or the mass migrations of the Irish.

The past is prologue, however. We must struggle with the facts of the present and the outlook for the future. What are the processes whereby leaders of many kinds are becoming aware of the tasks which lie ahead?

Several influences are awakening us to the population setting of our era and its population problems. I should like to name seven and then proceed to discuss policies and actions which seem to be emerging.

1. *The first influence results from a far greater knowledge of the facts of population changes.* Not only have methods of determining the actual numbers of people and the numbers of births and deaths been refined, but new methods of analysis are being developed. Population figures are now carefully studied by increasing numbers of trained people in an increasing number of countries. The figures indicate a mobility of people, particularly from rural areas to urban ones, almost all over the world; vast as this migration is, there are nevertheless increasing numbers of people in rural areas as well as great reservoirs of the poor in the cities. The figures show the proportions of the population in the different age groups, with the populations of most developing countries loaded with children and youth. The burdens of providing for the young, who now live longer, fall not only on parents but on governments. More food, more jobs, more schools, more doctors, more everything are not only needed—they are demanded.

Analyses of population figures also show the numbers of people in various occupational groups, the numbers of the gainfully employed as well as the unemployed and the underemployed. They indicate many problems relating to the needs for education, teaching new skills, and the economic burden of helping those who cannot find jobs.

Many facts about population which have been available for years in the Western industrialized countries are now becoming widely available in developing countries. To be sure, in some countries these facts are still inaccurate; yet it is safe to say that in most countries there is today a greater knowledge about the country's population than ever before. Significant, too, is the fact that the knowledge was developed by the countries themselves, not by outsiders.

2. *A second influence is the greater and ever-increasing knowledge of the reproductive process in human beings.* For economic reasons in part the subject has been under intensive study in animals for years, but only recently is receiving more serious attention by those scientists (physiologists, anatomists, biochemists, clinicians, psychiatrists, social scientists) equipped to investigate the functioning of the human body. Certainly, if scientists can learn to speed up the life-cycle enough that chickens lay many more eggs, cows produce their young at an earlier age, and that many farm animals are producing larger litters, they are capable of learning much more about the human reproductive cycle. Despite this lag, there is much new knowledge about both natural and artificial means of regulating pregnancy, the causes of sterility and malformations, the menstrual cycle, associated immunological and physiological phenomena, etc. The fact that there is more knowledge is undoubtedly a factor in the current interest in population affairs.

3. *There is a much greater understanding of the inter-relatedness of various factors in economic and social development.* Hypotheses concerning relations of economic and population trends have been and are being made and tested. Planning on all fronts is now popular and often considered essential. Again, basic data are often inadequate. Nevertheless, the relationships of the various factors involved in the economic, social, and population changes in all countries are under continuing study. The population dimension in the social, political, and economic changes is more and more clear. The effects of rapid population growth need discussion in many circles, and the circles need to meet more often. Certainly, the newly formed planning commissions need expert demographic advice. The economic and social implications of population trends for problems of agricultural production, for planning health and social welfare schemes, for planning housing and other services for urban development programs, for planning educational programs, for problems of trade and industrialization, for problems of manpower, employment, unemployment, and underemploy-

ment, for problems of migration, for a wider use of human resources —all need further exploration.

4. *A subtle factor, and one seldom mentioned, is the factor of the spirit.* Every culture has had its own sense of responsibility about its own people. In some, there is and has been traditionally, perhaps, more concern for the less fortunate than in others. But today's world is smaller. Countries do not stand alone. They have become more involved with each other. This involvement, this interdependence is making a subtle difference in their concerns for each other, even though the change may not be widely accepted. Somehow we have begun to realize that what happens to every other person in the world makes a difference to each of us. This concern may have been fathered in part by fear—fears of atomic wars, of East-West tensions, of the future— but it has unrealized, unexplored potentialities.

This greater concern is coupled with a greater demand for a better life for all. The revolution of rising expectations is common among the have-nots. Their demands are insistent. They are demanding that everything should happen immediately. Everything in the developing countries must happen yesterday! When the Russian educator proudly says, "It took only thirty years to educate our people," the Nigerian replies, "We can't wait that long."

5. *Man's growing ability to control natural resources is another factor.* It is the outcome of a much wider application of science and technology. Research in the physical and biological sciences has exploded. Growth in the social sciences is accelerating. "Research and development" are accepted activities of every large industrial complex. Applications of theoretical and basic research are well supported. Transfers and adaptations of this knowledge are being made to primitive societies. Modern medical science and public health are saving the lives of thousands who only a few short years ago would inevitably have died. Large new areas are being opened up for agricultural development. Industrial complexes are growing in societies that are still using primitive agricultural implements and techniques. Man reaches out to other planets; he splits atoms and genes. This explosion of knowledge, which apparently allows modern man to control his destiny, influences his attitudes toward population problems. Even in relatively primitive societies younger people begin to believe that they can do something about the future, that all does not lie in the hands of the gods. The traditional desire for large families

diminishes as opportunities for jobs, for having more of one's children grow up, for possessing more material goods increase.

6. *The policy implications of the amazing increases in rates of population growth are now more widely understood by international and national bodies.* The National Academy of Sciences in the United States, a conservative group of widely known scientists, pointed out in 1963 that world population "is likely to double in the next 35 years, producing a population of 6 billion by the year 2000. If the same rate of growth continues, there will be 12 billion people on earth in 70 years and over 25 billion by the year 2070. Such rapid population growth imposes a heavy burden on efforts to secure economic and social advance in the developing countries. Since we live in an interconnected world, this problem of population growth is also an international one that no one can escape." The Academy proceeded with detailed recommendations for immediate action.

Population facts are being looked at in all parts of the world by government policy makers as well as scientists. In Asia, the governments of the countries analyzed their own figures and debated the problems in the Asian Population Conference held in New Delhi, December, 1963, under the auspices of ECAFE (United Nations Economic Commission for Asia and the Far East). This was the first conference called by governments on the subject of population, and its mandate included recommendations to governments. Its cautious and rounded recommendations (later approved by the Commission) included three that are particularly relevant to the future developments in public health. The first was that governments "take account of the urgent need to adopt a positive population policy related to their individual needs." The second asked the Executive Secretary of ECAFE to "expand the scope of technical assistance available to governments in the region, upon their request, for data collection, research, experimentation and action in all aspects of population problems, including family welfare planning programmes, through regional advisory services, development and strengthening of regional, subregional and national training and research institutions, study tours, fellowships and meetings of technical groups." The third invited "the United Nations and the specialized agencies to expand the scope of the technical assistance they are prepared to give upon the request of governments in the development of statistics, research, experimentation and action programmes related to population."

This swift development of official population policy at the regional level within the United Nations' system is again a response to the facts of population pressure and population growth in the ECAFE region. Again, I should like to cite the summary figures that suggest the size and the depth of the problem there. The Asian portion of the ECAFE region includes Asia south of the Soviet Union and east of Iran. It includes more than half the population of the world and less than one-sixth of the land. In this area, the population numbered 1 billion in 1920 and 1.3 billion in 1950. The estimates of the United Nations indicate that the continuing decline of death rates along with unchanging birth rates will add a billion more people to the region between 1950 and 1980. Is the possibility of this added billion people real or simply another scare approach? It is indeed real—barring malnutrition, disease, and increasing death rates.

In this region, the governments of increasing numbers of countries realize that there is a critical need to reduce birth rates. Is this possible in a setting of village life, low income, subsistence agriculture, and illiteracy? Given only ancient medical knowledge and limited health services, the answer seemed to be somewhat in the negative direction. It is now obvious, though, that the future may move beyond ancient contraceptive techniques and hesitant health activities. There are advances in both natural and artificial means of regulating pregnancy. Motivation for small families is being strengthened within the Asian villages as the declining death rates, bringing with them the increasing numbers of children, exert pressures on land, jobs, and schools. Governments are becoming more active in what is now called "family welfare planning."

There need not be tragedy in Asia, but there are no immediate solutions to population problems as they now exist. Whatever the scientific and technical developments that concern both the means of regulating pregnancy and of influencing the motivations of families, popuation growth will long continue. The children who will be aged fifteen and over in 1975 are already born. The increasing numbers of people and families are continuing trends, though the rates of such increase will slow gradually if, when, and as birth rates decline. Decades are required for the solution of complicated, interwoven problems of population change and economic development. But the Asians see population growth as one of their important problems and decisions are being made country by country about what to do. Korea, Japan, India, Singapore, Pakistan have official government family planning programs. In Taiwan, Indonesia, Iran, Ceylon, and Thailand governments co-operate in various ways with action programs. Evidence of declines in birth rates is found in Taiwan, parts of India, Ceylon, and Japan.

7. *The final point I would like to make is that the mid-twentieth century has broken through the wall of silence about population growth.* There is now public discussion about these affairs among many groups. Those who seldom spoke to each other are exploring their areas of agreement and disagreement. Newspapers, TV shows, radio programs, magazines which shunned discussions of population in earlier years now discuss these affairs openly, not only in this country, but in Latin America, North Africa, and Asia. A recent official visitor to seven Latin American countries found church leaders, heads of governments and their planning commissions, and deans of medical schools all eager to discuss solutions—but not, as yet, talking freely to each other.

Wider discussion perhaps has brought an understanding too that the problems are not easy to solve. Certainly there is no one solution. Progress will have to be made on many fronts. There is no one solution any more than there is any one problem. Problems are different in every country, in different sections of many countries, and even in different groups within the same city or area. We have only to look at the difference between the underprivileged and the more privileged groups in this country to get a clear picture of these facts. The increased pressures for housing, schools, health, and social services, for the underprivileged in depressed areas, have taught us that rapid population increase is found commonly in areas of poor housing, inherited poverty, and juvenile delinquency.

Under these conditions, what policy makes sense in a democratic government, a pluralist society like ours? The way seems clear—and it is the way approved today by the U.S. government.

First of all, what we do and say must be based on a concern for human well-being and on facts uncovered by studies of the relations of population growth to economic and social development as well as on results of biomedical research programs now under way. Economic and social progress, laudable as they are, are not ends in themselves. Neither is slowing down, increasing or stabilizing population growth. They are means whereby countries as well as families enhance the development of healthy, self-reliant human beings. This development is fostered by equal opportunities for food, jobs, shelter, growth of innate capacities, service to others, and a sense of personal dignity. To achieve these ends there must be a healthy economy and social practices compatible with such opportunities.

To establish a balance between resources and numbers of people is a continuing problem. With high birth rates, particularly among those less able to provide for their families, this problem becomes acute.

Second, it must be recognized that there are many problems related to rapid population growth that affect many facets of the economy—unemployment, urban problems, needs for additional food, housing, education, health and social services; these same factors also affect the political aspirations of various groups, etc. There is no one solution to these problems which are obviously related to many factors beside the size of the population. A balanced program to raise the plans of economic, social, and family relationships is needed both at home and abroad.

Third, it is recognized that the decisions as to population policies and their implementation in other countries are to be made by individual countries and families in accord with their own needs and values. This is true in our own country, too. There is an ever wider recognition of both artificial and natural methods of regulating pregnancy, and they are increasingly being made freely available to all segments of the population. The U.S. government feels it desirable that all health facilities supported by public funds shall provide such freedom of choice, so that persons of all faiths are given equal opportunities to exercise their choice without offense to their consciences.

It is further realized that there are major needs for further knowledge in all fields related to population. More needs to be known about the specific relations of population growth to many phases of economic and social development, the means of extending awareness of population problems and changing movitations, and the methods of judging the effectiveness of various administrative organizations designed to cope with population problems; much more action research is needed in the natural and artificial methods of regulating pregnancy. There is obvious need to expand as rapidly as is scientifically feasible research laboratories devoted to the biomedical and biosocial aspects of human reproduction.

And finally, in accord with our government's support of the United Nations, its regional commissions, and specialized agencies, as well as the tradition of governmental co-operation with private groups and friendly governments, we stand ready to work co-operatively with such groups.

This is the setting: What are the tasks for the public health statesman? I suggest the following:

The first is to support, to promote, to give high priority to the extension of knowledge and of research in the many aspects of population problems. The United States has the facilities, the potential manpower, and the know-how with which to tackle complicated problems. Our best minds should be involved in population affairs. Research workers need to be trained in the biological, the medical, the social sciences. The National Academy of Sciences report has stated clearly what can be done in many fields. Workers need also to be trained, of course, to apply research findings.

Of particular interest to public health workers are the methods to be developed for carrying on and evaluating action programs, particularly those which attempt to involve large masses of people, such as are being sought in Asia. Public health analysts are only beginning to venture into these fields. What have they to transfer or to adapt from experience in other public health activities involving large segments of the population? In approaching this problem, let us not fail to heed the lesson repeatedly learned through other efforts in developing countries. What works here, particularly in administrative and educational practices, will not necessarily work there. The methods developed here may need considerable adaptation. That fact need not deter us in working on these problems both here and abroad. One of the most valuable products this country, and our universities in particular, has to offer is our pragmatic, problem-solving approach. We dig deep to find what works and what doesn't. We make hypotheses and find ways to test them. This approach, this experimental know-how is transferable. Let us share it more widely. But a word of caution is in order. Because of the peculiarly sensitive nature of population policies and practices the decisions of what to do must be those of the countries themselves.

A second contribution the public health statesman can make to the population problems arises from his long experience with many kinds of specialists, his ability to get them all to make their peculiar contributions to solving a problem. Each specialist sees population problems largely from his own vantage point and each believes in his solutions. The specialized health worker in the family planning field pushes ahead on developing and applying acceptable methods of limiting family size. The agriculturalist despairs of reducing the rate of population growth rapidly enough and so enjoins everyone, quite properly, to increase agricultural productivity, forgetting that it takes time as well to change age-old farming habits in tradition bound societies. Industrial development, postponement of the age of marriage, self-help, and education are held out by others as solutions, but these, too, take time. Still others argue for migration as a solution. I suggest that the public health statesman must accept the fact that there is no one answer, no one program for action. Certainly no more energy should be wasted on arguments among the specialists. Whether the specialist likes it or not, action will proceed on several fronts simultaneously. It will help if the inter-relations of the many facets of the problem are recognized, studied, and discussed. Here the public health statesman as well as leaders in private and public life have a role to play.

And finally, I suggest that the public health statesman has a peculiar responsibility in the problem of adjusting resources to the numbers of people they must support. This is because his success in prolonging life has helped make the problem more acute. It is also because he shares with political leaders a concern for all people, well or sick, rich or poor, old or young. The community is his patient, and today's overpopulation has become a problem that potentially affects all people, everywhere.

List of Participants

▪▪

HELEN ABBEY, Sc.D.
Associate Professor
Department of Biostatistics
School of Hygiene
The Johns Hopkins University

JOSEPH ALTER, M.D.
Lecturer
Public Health Administration
(International Health Studies)
School of Hygiene
The Johns Hopkins University

ROLANDO ARMIJO, M.D., M.P.H.
Professor
Department of Epidemiology
Escuela de Salud Publica
Santiago, Chile

MARSHALL C. BALFOUR, M.D.
Medical Consultant
The Population Council

LEONA BAUMGARTNER, M.D.
Assistant Secretary of State and Assistant Administrator of Human Resources and Social Development, Agency for International Development

BERNARD BERELSON, Ph.D.
Vice-President
The Population Council

EDGAR BERMAN, M.D.
Chief Health Consultant for Latin America, Agency for International Development

WILLARD BOYNTON, M.D.
Public Health Physician, Agency for International Development

MARGARET BRIGHT, Ph.D.
Associate Professor
Department of Chronic Diseases
School of Hygiene
The Johns Hopkins University

HOMER CALVER
Consultant in Public Health
The Hugh Moore Fund

ALICE CHENOWETH, M.D.
Chief
Division of Health Services
Children's Bureau
Department of Health, Education, and Welfare

ROBERT COOK
President
Population Reference Bureau

LESLIE CORSA, JR., M.D.
Director
Maternal and Child Health
State of California

JOHAN ELIOT, M.D.
Assistant Professor
Maternal and Child Health
School of Public Health
University of Michigan

HERMAN ENGEL
Planned Parenthood-World Population

241

RUTH FINKELSTEIN, M.D.
Consulting Gynecologist
Baltimore City Health Department

MOYE W. FREYMANN, M.D.
Consultant in Health
The Ford Foundation, India

ALAN F. GUTTMACHER, M.D.
President
Planned Parenthood-World Population

PAUL A. HARPER, M.D.
Professor and Head
Department of Maternal
    and Child Health and Population
    Dynamics
School of Hygiene
The Johns Hopkins University

DAVID M. HEER, Ph.D.
Assistant Professor of Demography
    and Biostatistics
School of Public Health
Harvard University

REUBEN HILL, Ph.D.
Director and Professor of Sociology
University of Minnesota

JOHN C. HUME, M.D.
Associate Dean
School of Hygiene
The Johns Hopkins University

JOHN W. C. JOHNSON, M.D.
Assistant Professor
Gynecology and Obstetrics
The Johns Hopkins Hospital

LEO A. KAPRIO, M.D.
Director
Division of Public Health Services
World Health Organization, Geneva

ALLYN W. KIMBALL, Ph.D.
Professor and Head
Department of Biostatistics
School of Hygiene
The Johns Hopkins University

DUDLEY KIRK, Ph.D.
Director

Demographic Division
The Population Council

HUGH LEAVELL, M.D.
Consultant
The Ford Foundation, India

PHILIP R. LEE, M.D.
Director, Health Services
Office of Human Resources and
    Social Development, AID. Agency
    for International Development

JOHN MAIER, M.D.
Associate Director
The Rockefeller Foundation

BERWYN MATTISON, Ph.D.
Executive Director
The American
    Public Health Association

OFELIA MENDOZA, Ph.D.
Field Director
International Planned
    Parenthood Federation

HUGH MOORE
President
The Hugh Moore Fund

MINORU MURAMATSU, M.D.
Institute of Public Health, Tokyo
    and School of Hygiene
The Johns Hopkins University

FRANK W. NOTESTEIN, Ph.D.
President
The Population Council

MANUEL E. PANIAGUA, M.D.
Medical Director
Planned Parenthood Association of
    Puerto Rico

CLIFFORD A. PEASE, M.D.
Special Assistant for
    Scientific Affairs
Office of International Research
National Institute of Health

J. Y. PENG, M.D.
Department of Preventive Medicine
School of Medicine
University of Washington

STEVEN POLGAR, Ph.D.
Director of Social Research
Planned Parenthood-World Population

KAMARAZU NARASIMHA RAO,
   M.B., B.S., M.D.
Additional Director General of
   Health Services
Government of India

ROWLAND V. RIDER, Sc.D.
Associate Professor
Department of Maternal
   and Child Health
School of Hygiene
The Johns Hopkins University

RICHARD L. RILEY, M.D.
Professor and Head
Department of Environmental
   Medicine
School of Hygiene
The Johns Hopkins University

NAFIS IFFAT SADIK, M.B., B.S.
Health Section
National Planning Commission
Pakistan

SHELDON J. SEGAL, Ph.D.
Director
Bio-Medical Division
The Population Council

M. C. SHEPS, M.D.
Professor

Department of Preventive Medicine
University of Pittsburgh

ERNEST L. STEBBINS, M.D.
Dean
School of Hygiene
The Johns Hopkins University

J. M. STYCOS, Ph.D.
Director
International Population Program
Cornell University

IRENE B. TAEUBER, Ph.D.
Senior Research
   Demographer
Princeton University

MATTHEW TAYBACK, Sc.D.
Deputy Commissioner of Health
Baltimore City Health Department

CARL E. TAYLOR, M.D.
Professor and Head
Division of International Health
School of Hygiene
The Johns Hopkins University

FRANCES H. TRIMBLE, M.D.
Medical Director
Planned Parenthood
Association of Baltimore

J. M. YANG, M.D., M.P.H.
Chairman
Planned Parenthood Federation
   of Korea
Professor
Department of Preventive Medicine
Yonsei University
Seoul, Korea

Index